TOWARDS A
Good Beginning

TOWARDS A

Good Beginning

TEACHING EARLY
CHILDHOOD MATHEMATICS

GRACE M. BURTON

⫙ Addison-Wesley Publishing Company
Menlo Park, California • Reading, Massachusetts
London • Amsterdam • Don Mills, Ontario • Sydney

This book is published by the Addison-Wesley
Innovative Division.

Design: Andrew Ogus
Cover design: Ellen Schmutz
Illustrations: Evanell Towne

ISBN 0-201-20086-4
ABCDEFGH-DO-8987654

contents

foreword   viii

one

positive teaching: a worthwhile goal   x

    The Impact of Teachers • The Years Before School • Parents as Partners • Goals for Kindergarten Mathematics Programs

two

still seeking synthesis   9

    Looking Back • Looking around

three

who are the children?   22

    The Education of Children with Special Needs • The Mentally Retarded Child • The Perceptually Handicapped Child • The Learning Disabled Child • The Orthopedically Handicapped Child and the Health-Impaired Child • The Emotionally Handicapped Child • The Gifted Child • All Together Now

four

classification: the first component   37

    Classification Materials • Classification Tasks

five

seriation: the second component   45

    Seriation Materials and Tasks

six

patterning: going a step beyond   48

    A Theoretical Point of View • Types of Patterns • Patterning Activities • Why Patterning?

seven

describing relationships 53

In the Beginning • Equivalence Relationships

eight

rote counting 57

The Size of the Task • Books • Fingerplays, Verses, and Songs

nine

writing the numerals 69

The Fading Technique • Penmanship Prerequisites • Reversals
• Dominance Tests • Instructional Techniques

ten

recognizing the numerals 79

Making It Meaningful • A Word on Behalf of Zero • An Awareness
Exercise

eleven

developing the concept of number 91

The Conservation of Number • Helping Children • The Counting Task
• Rational Counting Activities

twelve

vocabulary development 109

A Basic Word List • Technical Problems

thirteen

individual assessment techniques 112

The Idea of Diagnosis • Considerations Concerning Remediation

fourteen

two elementary operations: addition and subtraction 125

Models for Addition • Models for Subtraction • The Case of 3 — 5

fifteen

geometry 147

Skills at Kindergarten Entrance • Preparing a Foundation for Later Work
• Games and Activities

sixteen

early experiences in measurement   **155**

Incoming Skills • What *Is* Measurement? • Special Problems of the Learning-Disabled Child • Measurement Activities

seventeen

a special activity: graphing   **168**

eighteen

teaching the number facts: no frustration necessary   **173**

nineteen

teaching place value   **179**

Types of Materials • Using Place Value Devices in Remediation

twenty

developing skill with the addition and subtraction algorithms   **188**

Alternative Algorithms • Using Manipulative Materials • Using Pencil and Paper • Mechanical Aids to Calculation • Developing Skills

twenty-one

fractions: bridging the understanding gap   **205**

twenty-two

a few final words   **210**

Problem Solving—the Ultimate Goal • The Total Teacher • Characteristics of a Good Program

appendices

A.   Expectations of Experienced Kindergarten Teachers   **216**
B.   Some Suppliers of Mathematics Resources   **218**
C.   Anxious About a Math Word? Maybe This Glossary Will Help   **219**
D.   Some Psychological Terms: Applications in the Math Classroom   **228**
E.   Inexpensive Materials Useful for Teaching Mathematics   **232**
F.   Writing a Lesson Plan   **234**
G.   Commandments for a Math Teacher   **238**
H.   NCTM/NSCM Ten Basic Skill Areas   **239**
I.   All You Will Need to Know About Metric   **241**

references   **243**

index   **251**

foreword

John Dewey, in his important book *How We Think* (1933, p. 34), described the role of the teacher of young children:

> To keep alive the sacred spark of wonder and to fan the flame that already glows. His problem is to protect the spirit of inquiry, to keep it from becoming blase from over-excitement, wooden from routine, fossilized through dogmatic instruction, or dissipated by random exercise upon trivial things.

These words argue for a systematic mathematics curriculum that builds on the nature and the interests of the child, and it is hoped that this book will give early childhood preservice teachers the background they need to design such a program.

This book was written to help the preservice teacher provide appropriate mathematics experiences for all children operating at the primary level. Such children may be those we expect to progress at a customary pace through the school curriculum; those we think are capable of acceleration; and those who for a variety of reasons will need to spend longer than usual on fact, concept, or skill learning. The fundamental ideas of mathematics are the same for all; the teaching strategies and the time allotments are what must be planned with the individual in mind. Therefore, this book is as appropriate for the student majoring in special education as the student preparing to teach in a "regular" classroom setting. For all children, regardless of physical or mental condition, we must try to foster rather than eradicate each child's innate sense of wonder. Teachers can do this by developing a mathematics program that respects, in a fundamental sense, the fact that children learn by *doing* and will continue to "do" as long as the classroom climate is supportive.

Many of us proclaim that the young don't appreciate youth enough. The shame of it is many teachers don't appreciate youth either. They pretend that if adults can learn concepts in a certain way, kindergarteners can learn them in the same way. If adults can work quietly at a desk for hours at a stretch, a first grader should be able to duplicate that behavior without strain. If adults can learn without talking to their peers, the five-year-old should be able to do so as well. It isn't even as though it were harder, or more expensive, to teach math in a humane and human way. It takes a little thought and, at first, a little time. The rewards are tangible, however, if you accept as tangible the goosebumps you feel as a child whispers, "Guess what *I* found out!"

A mathematics curriculum that builds on the nature of the child differs from a traditional program of studies in several ways. There is a minimum of stress on pencil-and-paper activity and a maximum of involvement with real materials, both commercial and noncommercial. Instead of a headlong rush to fact memorization, a child-centered mathematics curriculum places an emphasis on individual exploration of material and discovery of patterns and invariants in number and in material. The time children spend in such exploration is no more wasted than is the time spent on building a solid foundation for a tall building or laying a true keel for a seagoing vessel.

It may seem unrealistic to ask that a teacher take into consideration the unique qualities of each young learner and help each to develop mathematical structures in his or her own mind. But I believe the world will be better for those of us who dream of humanizing mathematics instruction for young children, who sing boldly of that dream, and who do whatever we can to bring it to reality.

None of us, however, brings such a dream to reality without the support of others. Four people who have been my support deserve a public thank-you. Should he read this book, Vin Glennon will recognize his influence in matters pertaining to mathematics education. His vision kindled mine, and I hope he will be content that I have not misconstrued his messages. Conversations with J. Dan Knifong sharpened my view in particular areas, notably those of teaching the fundamental operators, developing a schema for assuring memorization of the number facts, and developing skills with the addition and subtraction algorithms. His clear thinking and careful reasoning made a significant contribution to those sections. And in a special way I thank Michael Burton and Becky Burton. As they pursued their own dreams they had the courage to let their mother pursue hers. Their growing into compassionate, interesting, and genuinely good individuals daily renews my optimism about the fate of the world.

one

positive teaching:
a worthwhile goal

> Discovering how to make something comprehensible to the young is only a continuation of making something comprehensible to ourselves in the first place . . . understanding and aiding others to understand are both of a piece.
>
> Jerome S. Bruner (1966, 38)

the impact of teachers

The child entering school for the first time is, in every sense of the word, an unfulfilled promise. The teacher who looks out on the twenty-five or so faces gathered in a circle that first day is often struck with the enormity of the task ahead. The importance of a good beginning on any human or curriculum dimension cannot be overstated, but this book focuses on only one of them, helping children to a good start in mathematics. That this subject is feared by many adults is far from news, but most young children do not harbor any negative feelings towards this important area of human learning. It is essential for the teacher to assure that during the first school years children develop excitement and curiosity about counting and measuring. A supportive climate is a fragile thing. It will be maintained only if teachers are aware of all the messages, both verbal and nonverbal, that they are sending—a pained expression, an exasperated sigh, or a humorous remark tinged with sarcasm will quickly destroy even the most carefully established rapport.

Towards this end, teachers must approach mathematics in a positive way, apply their creative talents to the teaching of the subject, and make a conscious decision to avoid the rush to the pencil-and-paper mathematics that is seen in so many early childhood classrooms. Effective mathematical growth is slow and requires a solid foundation of prenumber and early number activities. Emphasis on recording concepts that are only faintly understood is the first step towards later mathematical difficulties and failures.

Positive teaching takes patience and a commitment to the idea that children learn differently from adults, that they need to build up their own mathematical ideas, and that ideas cannot be handed to or told to them. It assumes that children are active, willing learners and that teachers perceive learning mathematics as a joint and joyful adventure between teacher and child.

the years before school

The environment of the preschool child is far from unmathematical. Over a generation ago, investigators in the area of child development (Ilg and Ames 1951, 4-5) studied children from one to five years old and generated a list of mathematical abilities possessed by the children at each age level. Although their sample was composed of children somewhat above the average in intelligence, it was also collected over thirty years ago, before the advent of educational TV.

1 year   "One-by-one" pattern (the rudiment of counting) of manipulating one object after another, consecutively. Can release one cube into a cup.

18 months   Can build a tower of 3-4 cubes. Ten cubes into a cup. Uses the word *"more."*

2 years   Distinguishes between one and many, but usually does not count objects. Says "anudder." Idea of one more. Says "two balls" when handed a second ball. Can say "big ball" if big and little are presented. May want a cookie for each hand if given only one. Can build a tower of 6-7 cubes.

2½ years   Can give "just one" cube on request. May count by rote: "one, two, lots."

3 years   Can usually count to two objects. May or may not start with "one" when counting. Is reported to count to five. Can give "just one" or "just two" cubes on request. Activities may be influenced by numbers. May demand "three" or "four" of everything.

4 years   Counts with correct pointing to objects. Is reported to count to 10. May start with a number higher than one. Verbal counting without objects definitely exceeds counting of objects.

4½ years   Can give "just one," two, or three cubes on request. Counts with correct pointing to four objects and answers "how many?" Some can count ten objects. Understands the terms "most," "both," and "biggest" but not the terms "same" and "equal."

5 years   Counting by ones: one-third can count to 30 or better; the majority to 13. Asked how high they can count, some say 100; most name a figure in the teens or twenties. Most mistakes consist of not being able to go on after a 9.

How does a child learn so much without the benefit of direct teaching? The answer is found in the nature of children. From their earliest years, children investigate and discover. At a level appropriate to their mental development they observe, question, form hypotheses, collect data to test out these hypotheses, and draw conclusions based on the data collected. Children come to school with wide experiences in all of these areas. That experience is invaluable in helping them explore the world of shape, size, and quantity.

Children seem to be born curious and wanting to share their discoveries. Infants explore the world with their eyes and gurgle with delight at the mobile hanging over the crib. Toddlers wiggle beneath the coffee table to see if they can fit under it. Two-year-olds admire the set of graduated colored rings they have stacked. Three-year-olds put circular and square shapes into the appropriate openings in a "mailbox" over and over again. Four-year-olds who have watched older children pour milk from a bottle into a bowl copy the action and observe the milk overflow the bowl and cover the table. Five-year-old Mike observes cars passing by his house and ponders what would happen if wheels were not round. He makes up a song: "If wheels were square, we wouldn't get anywhere." And he sings it again and again, delighting in his creation. Another child builds a tower of blocks as high as the chair seat and calls to Dad to "come and see."

From the very beginning, the young child's world is full of number, geometry, and measurement. Because they naturally occur in the life of a child, these activities may be incorrectly deemed unimportant in setting the stage for mathematics. They are not. Experiences in which a child begins the exploration of the world of shape and size are the following.

Putting plates on the table.

Putting toys away in the proper place.

Stringing beads or buttons or macaroni.

Crawling under chairs and tables.

Climbing up trees and jungle gyms.

Running around a yard.

Curling up in a box.

Climbing up a ladder.

Moving furniture in a room.

Placing pans in a cupboard.

Crayoning on a piece of paper.

Unpacking groceries.

Trying on clothes.

Pouring sand or water from one container to another.

Balancing on a seesaw.

Being weighed and measured at the doctor's office.

Building with blocks.

Making pudding or fruit juice Popsicles.

Most children have been exposed to fundamental numerical, geometric, and measurement concepts long before they enter school. Boys and girls who lack these or similar experiences are less likely to have acquired the mathematical background necessary for success in the typical kindergarten program.

Of the many early experiences with counting and measurement, the most common one comes in the form of a question from adults: "How old are you?" Almost as soon as a child begins talking, parents and other friendly adults begin asking this question, even if it is clear to all concerned that the two-year-old cannot properly comprehend it. The child cannot yet understand long (or even short) periods of time or their measurement, usually has not learned to count, and may not even recognize *two* or *three* as number names. Adults typically "teach" the answer by giving it themselves and asking the child to repeat it and hold up "that many" fingers. Even when the child learns to say "three" through frequent lessons of this type, he or she has not acquired anything like the adult understanding of number or time. Yet the child *does* learn that there are things called numbers and that they are used to answer certain types of questions containing the phrases "how many" and "how much." The first of these phrases leads to counting and numbers, the second to measurement.

A systematic mathematics curriculum during the early childhood years should build on the nature and the interests of the children, who have been building up their own mathematical understandings since birth. The children sitting in early childhood classrooms are not blank chalkboards to be filled with the knowledge of the physical world. Rather they come with prior conceptualizations of the universe (Knifong 1973, 28), including the universe of number, geometry, and measurement.

Many of the activities found in the home environment can be adapted to the school setting in a room where children can creatively manipulate objects. The housekeeping area, the block center, the water and sand tables, and the commercial and teacher-made games and materials all provide hands-on resources for young students to explore the wonders of number, space, size, and shape. Teachers thoroughly acquainted with a variety of interesting experiences can create learning settings that stimulate creative exploration and foster active involvement.

parents as partners

One of the challenges and joys of the teacher in the early grades is working with parents. Because many parents have limited knowledge of what is "normal," it is helpful for the teacher to describe in a meeting or in a letter home what can be expected of children around the age of five. First-time parents are especially prone to expect too much of their child now that he or she is "big" and going to school.

Physical characteristics	*Psychological characteristics*
Body is lengthening and becoming less rounded.	Children are becoming self-sufficient in personal care routines.
Large muscles are generally well developed.	Eagerness to carry out assigned tasks is evident.
Fine muscles are beginning to develop.	Projects are planned before they are executed.
Eye-hand coordination is weak but improving.	Exploration with a variety of materials is eagerly embarked upon.
Children are apt to be far sighted.	Dramatic play is popular.
Energy level is high.	Group play is enjoyed.

Physical characteristics	*Psychological characteristics*
Handedness is quite well established.	Children are often protective of other boys and girls.
Attention span is gradually increasing.	Special friendships may develop.

Parents will appreciate being told of the important role they have played in preparing their children for the study of mathematics at school—lifting baby from the crib and saying "up-se-daisy," providing bathtub toys or containers of different shapes, encouraging water play, touching tiny toes and repeating, "this little piggie went to market," or gently extending baby's arms high in the air while saying "so big." Parents may never have considered these experiences intellectually valuable. They will be pleased to learn that asking children to "go upstairs," "look under the table," or "run fast" or asking them to help set the table or cut up food were preparation for learning mathematics. Parents who recognize this and are praised for their efforts are apt to be more alert to other situations that can be used to provide a basis for mathematics instruction.

The teacher walks a thin line between being helpful and being "bossy." For parents who seem eager to work with their children, however, a list of books to read to them (Young 1979) should not seem overly intrusive.

Those who ask "What else can I do?" might like to buy a copy of Mary Baratta-Lorton's *Workjobs for Parents* (1975). The low-key but well-planned activities in that book are a fine supplement to the mathematics program outlined in this text. A note of caution: even to well-meaning adults, many of the activities in the classroom or in books such as *Workjobs for Parents* may seem to be "just play." Researchers agree that such activities have tremendous positive impact on the intellectual development of children, especially in the areas of reasoning and language. Informing parents of the value of these deceptively frivolous games may make all the difference in how your attempts to provide an effective, enjoyable learning environment are supported.

A classroom for young children should be a laboratory for exploration and discovery both of the physical features of the real world and of the child's own social and psychological strengths. It may look far different from what parents think of as school. To encourage parents' wholehearted cooperation, teachers often send explanatory notes and sincere requests for assistance home with their students. One child-centered mathematics program in kindergarten, grade one, or grade two, *Mathematics Their Way* (Barrata-Lorton 1976), includes sample letters explaining the program, which you could use as models as you compose your own.

Encouraging the participation of parents in the school program can help you provide individual help to children and can foster good home-school relationships. Among the things parents can do are to help with art projects, read stories, bake or cook, and take small groups out to the playground. Some parents may be willing to share special talents such as singing, guitar playing, doing magic tricks, or telling stories to the whole class. Even in classrooms that have aides, there is always plenty for another pair of hands to do.

Some parents prefer to assist in ways that are not directly involved with children. Such parents might do clerical chores such as typing, running the ditto machine, assembling packets of seat work, or creating bulletin boards. Parents who are not able to come during the school day can feel a part of the classroom family if they are asked to make games for the children, repair bookcases, or contribute to special displays. Working on tasks together gives teachers and parents an opportunity to talk on an informal basis. Minor problems can often be cleared up in a few minutes' conversation; more difficult problems can be brought a step closer to solution each time caring adults discuss them in a noncombative manner.

Most parents want to help their children succeed. Most teachers do, too. Given these facts, working together is a natural.

goals for kindergarten mathematics programs

In 1902 E. H. Moore asked, "Would it not be possible for the children in the grades to be trained in power of observation and experiment and reflection and deduction so that always their mathematics should be directly connected with matters of thoroughly concrete character?" (1967, 367) The teacher of young children could do worse than to keep this question in mind and to show it *is* possible.

Today the majority of children entering the first grade will have at least one year of prior schooling. Even kindergarten entrants may have had several years of preschool. Because early childhood programs, like elementary programs, vary widely, it is unsafe to make the assumption that children who have had preschool experiences are necessarily better prepared for a formal mathematics program in kindergarten than children who have remained at home or who have stayed with sitters.

Kindergarten entrants may have acquired a variety of mathematical concepts and skills. Many five-year-olds can count up to ten objects, have a little knowledge of the ordinal numbers such as "second"; a penny but not a nickel or dime; some children can recognize the numerals to 5, and fewer can write the numerals to 5. There will be children, of course, who can do much more and others who will not even be able to identify colors or count to two. In general, kindergarten students from lower socioeconomic classes exhibit fewer academic skills at school entrance than do those of higher socioeconomic levels. This may be due to nutritional deprivation during prenatal and early childhood stages (Birch and Gussow 1970); lack of educational toys or books; or poorly developed listening, vocabulary, and inquiry skills (Miller and Camp 1972). Many health-impaired children live in less-than-ideal physical environments from prenatal days. In addition, their postnatal environment may provide neither the cognitive nor the biological conditions necessary for optimal growth.

What goals might the kindergarten teacher reasonably have? Appendix A displays the expectations of some experienced teachers. Although any such list of suggestions may be adapted to the local situation, the following are offered. The child will be able to:

Classify objects on the basis of size, shape, and color.

Copy and extend a pattern made with blocks or pictures.

Seriate a set of ten graduated rods.

Use and understand words such as *big, small, up, down, over, under, heavy, light, long, short, more, less,* and *same.*

Identify sets of "one more" and "one less" for sets up to nine.

Count rationally to ten.

Identify the first, second, third, fourth, and fifth items in a sequence.

Recognize the numerals to 10.

Identify sets of 0, 1, 2, 3, 4, and 5.

Match numerals from 1 to 5 with sets of one to five objects.

Identify and name a circle, a square, a triangle, and a rectangle.

Identify and name a penny, a nickel, and a dime.

Use nonstandard units to determine the weights and lengths of objects.

Make and interpret pictorial or bar graphs.

No matter how beautiful a set of goals you develop, bear in mind that they will probably not be appropriate for all children in your classroom. You are apt to have several children from home environments that have not stressed language development. Perhaps you will have a child with undiagnosed vision or hearing problems. You may have an exceptionally talented boy or girl and/or one who is mentally retarded. The children will also have various levels of emotional and physical development. Some will be able to stand much stress; some will collapse into tears or angry flailing at the least frustration. Some will be able to write their names; others will never have held a pencil. Some will be able to sit and attend for long periods of time; others may seldom sit still. Let a set of well-thought-out goals be your guide, but don't become angry with the children who cannot or will not conform. Patience and the creative use of alternate strategies will help you through the most difficult situations.

two

still seeking synthesis

In 1965 "And Now Synthesis: A Theoretical Model for Mathematics Education" by Vincent J. Glennon appeared in *The Arithmetic Teacher*. Judging by the events of the past nineteen years, it was a publication ahead of its time. Perhaps the present Zeitgeist is more favorable to its message: What is needed in mathematics education is "an integration of the thesis of *content* with the antithesis of *method* to form a higher union, a synthesis in mathematics education" (p. 141). Glennon believed that the questions, "What mathematics should I teach?" and "How should I teach mathematics?" "form the warp and woof of the fabric of the professional study of mathematics education" (p. 136). Consideration of the various extreme answers to each of these questions was valuable, he stated, because extremists "show us where the edges of the road are. It is as helpful to know what does not work as it is to know what does work" (p. 141).

The problems elementary school teachers face are both unique to the time and common to the task. Lessons from the past can not only help us meet the challenges of the present but can also, in the process, help us reach that synthesis that has long been missing in the profession of mathematics education.

looking back

the colonial era (1620—1789)

In the days of colonial settlement, three essentially different educational patterns were found in the three areas of population density: New England, the mid-Atlantic region, and the southern colonies. Those who came to the new land sought either to acquire wealth or avoid religious prosecution. Both these goals affected colonial education. Education for young children began officially in New England when the Old Deluder Law was passed in 1647. In order to protect children against that old deluder, Satan, the General Court of the Colony of Massachusetts decreed that each township of fifty households or more should appoint someone to teach the children of that township reading and writing. The third "R" was omitted from consideration. Attendance was not compulsory, but children of both sexes attended, often at different hours or seasons, as soon as they were old enough to "stand and keep their place."

In the mid-Atlantic colonies, schools were primarily organized for the same reason: children must be able to read the Bible. After 1636, however, cyphering was included in the curriculum. Boys and girls studied reading, writing, arithmetic, and catechism.

In the South, education was provided by private tutors for the children of the rich. No education was provided for poor students. The curriculum depended upon the abilities of the tutor and/or the wishes of the parents. Reading and writing were the subjects most likely to be stressed.

The teachers of the period were usually busy housewives, unmarried or widowed women of the middle class, indentured servants, apprentice teachers, retired clergymen, or young men not yet ready to enter a "real" profession. Whether and how mathematics was taught was very dependent on what texts and training, if any, the teachers had. The level of the latter was usually low. Benjamin Franklin had suggested, for example, that some of the poorer graduates of the academies would make suitable teachers.

There was urgent need for tradesmen with facility in computation and measurement. Those who acquired these skills did so largely on their own, however, using books designed for self-study like *The Young Man's Companion* or a borrowed Hodder, Greenwood, or Cocker arithmetic.

If little attention was given to content, less was given to teaching method. A procedure determined worthy of study was demonstrated, and then problems were given for the student to solve. When they were well solved, they were copied into "manuscript arithmetics" (Woody 1929). No time was wasted sugar coating the task; students were expected to apply themselves and make the most of their limited time in school. Those few boys planning to enter the Latin Grammar School or the vocational academies were expected both to learn the arithmetic they would need to pursue further studies and acquire good study habits. There was small accommodation to individual differences or desires. In mathematics, as in life, students were to learn the rules and apply them correctly.

the early national period (1789—1865)

By the middle of this period arithmetic was firmly established as an elementary school subject, its content dictated by the book the teacher used. The most popular text in the newly united states was Thomas Dilworth's *The Schoolmaster's Assistant,* first published in England in 1742. The first American edition was reprinted thirty years later and remained in wide use until at least 1818. Another popular text was Daboll's *Schoolmaster's Assistant,* first printed in this country in New London, Connecticut, in 1799 or 1800 (sources vary). By 1831, it had gone through eighty editions. Both texts were devoted to the study of computational procedure presented in the deductive fashion (rules are given with many examples to be worked) and the solution of word problems. Special editions printed on fine paper and elegantly bound were sometimes made for use by young ladies.

In several ways, the content of arithmetics of the time, whether published in England or the United States, continued to reflect the national attitude that to be practical was to be good and that pampering young learners was unnecessary. Texts contained very few explanations or written passages and no pictures at all until 1830. A problem or two worked out as an example was followed by a collection of unsolved problems to be completed in similar manner. Scant attention was given to motivating students or to relieving the tediousness of the task. Another popular arithmetic of the early 1800s was Pike's *New Complete System of Arithmetic,* printed in 1788 and heartily endorsed by George Washington. It begins with three pages on the reading and writing of numbers. This is followed by three pages on addition—up to twelve ten-digit numbers are added—followed by three pages on subtraction. Then multiplication is attacked. The first multiplication example is 2×37934. On the third page devoted to multiplication are six examples under the heading "Multiplication

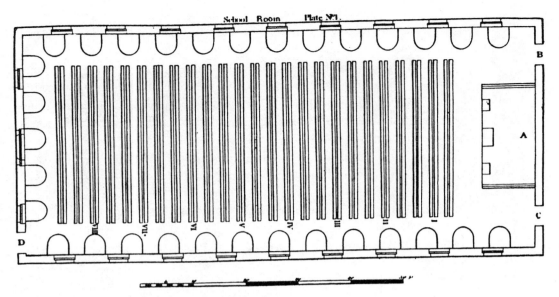

Figure 2–1   *Plan of a Lancastrian school room*

less than 12." One of the six examples is 9152 × 760483. For the next fifty years to be able to "figure Pike's" was proof of great scholarship (Woody 1929).

This was not a time of methodological stagnation, however. During this period many innovations were seen. The first graded series was published in the 1820s, for example. Colburn, Pike, Ray, and Adams all divided the arithmetic content into two or more books, the first of which usually covered the entire elementary school span. This was a first attempt to impose scope and sequence through curricular material. It was not entirely successful, however, because textbook ownership was still an individual responsibility. In a class of fifty students, most of the thirty-four extant books might be available—at the rate of one copy of each.

In 1821 the first alternative to the use of the deductive method was presented. Its advocate was Warren Colburn. In his *First Lessons in Intellectual Arithmetic on the Plan of Pestalozzi*, Colburn stressed mental discipline and an inductive approach. Pestalozzi, a Swiss educator greatly inspired by Rousseau, believed children should be involved in direct experience with what they are learning about and that the subject matter should be adapted to the child's environment and state of development. Under this plan, which Pestalozzi attempted to demonstrate with fifty

Figure 2–2   *A Lancastrian student monitor's seat and desk*

abandoned children, the study of numbers began with the children's manipulation of objects. The role of the teacher was to ask the right questions rather than to merely dictate a rule. Colburn's book became extremely popular, selling more than one million copies in the first fifty years following its publication (Cubberley 1919).

During the period from 1812 to 1830, a radically different method of providing instruction was tried. Although it had limited lasting impact on the development of modern elementary schools, the Lancastrian plan represented a systematic approach to meeting the dual problem of few trained teachers and many pupils. Under it, the teacher had charge of 200 to 1000 students in a single room (Cubberley 1919) and appointed monitors from among each group of ten or so. These "youthful corporals" would then "hear the lessons" of their peers. Once a student had learned a group's assigned subject, he or she would "move up" to the next group. This became the official method of instruction in eight New York cities by 1828 and was also popular in Pittsburgh, Baltimore, Richmond, and many other metropolitan areas. Discipline was stern, and the emphasis was on training the powers of the mind by means of rote learning. Arithmetics written specifically for Lancastrian schools were published. Primitive as his solution now seems, Joseph Lancaster was one of the first educators who considered instructional methodology from the point of view of efficiency—an important perspective, as the number of students rapidly increased.

the post-civil war period (1865-1900)

Following the Civil War, the number of students in the common schools grew dramatically. In addition to the predictable rise in population, former slaves, both adults and children, sought the skills that had long been denied them—literacy and the tools with which to acquire economic security. Learning the mathematics prerequisite to agricultural and industrial vocations was a priority. In addition, a new reason to include the study of this topic was espoused. It was generally believed that the mind was like a muscle; the more it was exercised, the stronger it would be. Although as old as Plato and Aristotle (they also believed that mathematics, an abstract subject requiring concentration and memorization, was an ideal vehicle for the development of mental prowess), this theory swept the educational world. Topics with little practical or theoretical value were assigned because they were believed helpful in the attainment of a strong mind. Thus, proficiency at rapid mental calculations and extensive, involved world problems became respected goals of the elementary curriculum.

One radical departure from traditional curriculum organization was suggested by the German educator W. W. Grube. In his method, a complete study of the numbers 1 through 10 was undertaken during the first year of school. Each number was developed, one at a time, using all four operations. Some American texts published in the 1870s and 1880s espoused the Grube technique, but its overall impact was only a brief flurry of interest (Cubberley 1919).

Concurrently there was a groundswell of concern for discovering how a child learns best. For the first time, authors of arithmetics were declaring they had studied the child's mind and had applied the fruits of those investigations to the study of arithmetic. Graded texts became more popular, and the correct placement of content was a topic of much lively debate.

Scientists in the infant discipline of psychology also began to turn their attention to education. One of these, G. Stanley Hall, declared that the school should adapt to the child rather than the reverse. Proponents of Hall's thesis believed that if the child's interests and intellectual development were considered when instruction was planned, the child was likely to learn better. To this end, illustrations, child-centered story problems, and guided discovery lessons began to appear in texts. As foundations of educational practice began to be studied, William James's *Principles of Psychology* (1890) provided a bridge between psychology and education. In 1896, just six years after its publication, John Dewey, strongly influenced by James, opened an experimental school in which children learned mathematics through solving problems of immediate interest to them. His "progressive education" flourished for thirty years and laid the groundwork for many later educational programs.

During this same period, mathematicians in Europe began developing theories that would have a profound influence on elementary school arithmetic. Mathematics had been regarded as a practical tool, and mathematical ideas were considered important because they could be used to express relationships between objects in the physical world. Now mathematicians began to examine their discipline in a new light as a logical system based on a set of assumptions. They reexamined even basic concepts such as that of *five*, stating that although the number tells something about a group of objects, it is not dependent upon the physical existence of such a group. This deceptively simple pronouncement heralded a return to the Platonian philosophy that *five* exists separate from objects. It followed that an examination of the essential nature of number itself and a determination of what is necessary to build a firm foundation for mathematics would be appropriate. Mathematicians set about that task.

the early twentieth century (1900—1957)

By 1910 compulsory school attendance to age fourteen or sixteen was law in all but six states. By 1918 these six had joined the rest. In addition, thousands of young immigrants whose parents saw the United States as a land of opportunity swelled the school population. In the schools of the twentieth century, two radically different schools of psychology became dominant. Both attempted to answer the question "How can children best learn mathematics?", and the answers of each school have had a significant and continuing impact on mathematics education.

One of the theories, the "connectionism" of E. L. Thorndike, was a modern embodiment of the empiricist philosophy of John Locke. In his early writings, Thorndike stated that mathematics was a body of fact and that a separate "connection" must be formed in the mind of the child for each fact to be learned. He felt that although "understanding the facts" would help children memorize them, securing that memorization was the responsibility of the teacher:

> It is not safe to assume that the rank and file of a class will form bonds of their own initiative, even in cases that seem to us very easy. They seem easy to us, in fact, partly because we have them already formed.

> Thus, it is not safe to assume that the formation of the bonds $9+4=13$ and $6\times9=54$ will insure the formation of $4+9=13$ and $9\times6=54$. In general, the reverses of the combinations need some separate attention and drill. It is not safe to assume that pupils who can respond to $54=$. . . 9's and $63=$. . . 9's perfectly will be able to respond perfectly to $58=$. . . 9's and . . . remainder $70=$. . . 9's and . . . remainder. On the contrary, it is much safer to assume that the three out of four will not (Thorndike 1921, 64).

Great stress was put on speed and accuracy in the processes important in adult daily life (Reed 1927). Drill in many forms was employed so that the desired bonds would be formed.

At the opposite end of the continuum were educators like Dewey who believed that arithmetic was a valuable tool for solving problems and that children learned arithmetic best when it met present needs and interests. In "progressive" schools, arithmetic was to be taught incidentally, as a particular concept or process was required by a project. The teacher was not to impose a preset curriculum; children were to be awakened to an interest in mathematics through a nurturing of their inherent curiosity. A page from John Stone's arithmetic text for children illustrates the philosophy:

> That the child may delight in his work, see that it is useful to him in his play and in his little daily affairs, and wish to know more of number from day to day, there are many little rhymes, number stories, and simple descriptions of games. These are not given for the sake of the drill they contain, but to secure and to hold the child's interest in his study of number. For it is expected that many or all of them will suggest similar things that the child will wish to do with number, and thus they will suggest real "projects" in the true sense of that much-used and over-used term (1930, iii & iv).

The Deweyan philosophy was supported by the emergence of Gestalt psychology. To Gestaltists, learning took place when new information was fitted into the knowledge already possessed by the learner. Seeing an overall pattern gave added meaning to the individual parts. "The whole is more than the sum of its parts" was the shibboleth of Gestalt psychologists. They believed it was gaining an awareness of patterns that was important in the study of mathematics—not the memorization of isolated facts. Encouraging the discovery of the meanings of mathematical truths was therefore an important role of the teacher. Concrete materials designed to make the structure of the number system visible were deemed valuable. One such set was developed by Catherine Stern. Her emphasis on structure is not surprising; she was once a research assistant of Max Wertheimer, one of the founders of Gestalt psychology.

An outspoken advocate for teaching arithmetic "meaningfully" was William H. Brownell. Several advantages to this method were claimed in a classic article written in the late 1940s, but Brownell had held essentially the same position for over twenty years. Teaching arithmetic meaningfully, Brownell stated, has the following virtues for the student:

1. Gives assurance of retention.
2. Equips him with the means to rehabilitate quickly skills that are temporarily weak.
3. Increases the likelihood that arithmetical ideas and skills will be used.
4. Contributes to ease of learning by providing a sound foundation and transferable understandings.
5. Reduces the amount of repetitive practice necessary to complete learning.
6. Safeguards him from answers that are mathematically absurd.
7. Encourages learning by problem solving in place of unintelligent memorization and practice.
8. Provides him with a versatility of attack which enables him to substitute equally effective procedures for procedures normally used but not available at the time.
9. Makes him relatively independent so that he faces new quantitative situations with confidence.
10. Presents the subject in a way which makes it worthy of respect. (1947, 263-264)

On the other hand, Brownell believed teaching guided by Thorndike's connectionist theory had several weaknesses:

1. Our attention as teachers is directed away from the processes by which children learn, while we are overconcerned about the product of learning.
2. Our pace of instruction is too rapid, while we fail to give learners the aids they need to forestall or surmount difficulty.
3. We provide the wrong kinds of practice to promote sound learning.
4. Our evaluation of error and our treatment of error are superficial. (1944, 148)

These divergent psychological stances affected the *way* elementary school mathematics was taught. The arithmetic content had remained relatively stable, however. This situation was about to change.

the post-sputnik era (1957—1976)

In 1957 the Soviet Union dealt the United States' image a major blow by launching the first man-made satellite. As Sputnik orbited the earth, challenging the United States' position as a leader in the scientific world, Americans everywhere were asking, "Why weren't *we* first?" A major shift in content was decreed imperative.

Many forces influenced the curriculum developers: an awareness of the research into mathematical foundations that had taken place over the last 100 years, an understanding of mathematics at an advanced level, and disdain for the many classroom teachers who understood neither the essence of the subject matter nor the techniques of teaching it beyond the drill approach. Curriculum developers believed that school mathematics should prepare students to take a role, either as active leaders or as knowledgeable followers, in our increasingly quantitative culture, and they set about developing school programs that would produce enlightened citizens for the space age.

The curriculum developing task was begun, funded by huge amounts of government money, and those who were chosen as developers were for the most part university-level mathematicians. As a result, in the "new math," the emphasis was on the theory, and practical applications were often ignored. As soon as the ink was dry on the first drafts, they were tested in classrooms by teachers with little or no training in the advanced content underlying the new curriculum.

Despite claims that it would help children attain a deeper understanding of the explanations behind the rules of the real number system and of the principles of elementary geometry, the new math was often taught in a "memorize-this-and-do-that" manner. Such practices are not apt to invite involved exploration of mathematical structure or the discovery of mathematical relationships. The use of these techniques, however, is not inconsistent with the truism that teachers tend to teach the way they have been taught and tend to teach most poorly that which they have learned least well. For most teachers mathematics was not a subject they were especially comfortable with on either side of the desk. Although a minority of elementary teachers who were trained recently and well in mathematics enjoyed teaching the new topics, most approached the prescribed changes in content with a combination of fear, trepidation, anxiety, hope, ignorance, and confusion that was equaled only by that of the general public to whom they were supposed to explain this phenomenon. Although inservice programs were frequently offered, many teachers taught new math with little or no preparation or readily available ongoing assistance.

An entirely different approach to education, sprung from the theory of Thorndike, was also popular during the 1950s and 1960s. In his quiet Harvard office, B. F. Skinner had earlier developed both a system called programmed instruction and "teaching machines" for independent use by students. The ultimate "teacher-proof" material was developed by Carl Bereiter and Seigfried Engleman. Distar was designed for use with children described as "culturally deprived," a population of primary concern to educators of these "New Society" years. A word-by-word, action-by-action script was given the teacher, who needed only to follow it. Language development, small-group work, constant repetition, and frequent verbal reinforcement were features of the program. The use of concrete objects and discovery were not allowed. There was little concern for the structure of the number system, or for the "whys" of the procedures. All attention was centered on helping these children catch up with middle-class youngsters. Less extreme versions of reinforcement-based instruction were also a part of the mathematics scene during this time, usually in the form of self-paced booklets or packets of work. The content, although laced with the flavor of new math, was apt to be the familiar mathematics of the 1950s.

the back-to-basics movement (1976—   )

Concurrent with the bicentennial celebration, a new wave of mathematics education crested. Falling achievement scores and a growing assertiveness on the part of parents provided the perfect setting for the "back-to-basics" movement. It enjoyed immediate acceptance among large segments of the public. Repeating a rallying cry is easier than researching its validity. There was little discussion about just what the basics we were to go back to were. In the absence of other definitions, the arithmetic of the 1800s (stress on computation with whole numbers and fractions) has somehow been accepted as basic. Although these essential topics were included in even the most revolutionary of the new math programs, they tended to be overshadowed as attempts to develop mathematical concepts received more attention than developing proficiency in the use of the traditional algorithms.

An additional facet of the back-to-basics movement was the insistence on a constellation of classroom practices, including a new emphasis on teacher authority, discipline, and traditional values. Learning by doing was in large part replaced by sitting and studying, which marked a methodological return to pre-Deweyan days.

The back-to-basics trend has alarmed many mathematics educators who see the movement as a new trial of what has not worked before. A major professional organization, the National Council of Teachers of Mathematics, has attempted to restore balance to the situation. A set of "New Basics" (Appendix H) was promulgated first in 1975 by one of its affiliate groups, the National Council of Supervisors of Mathematics. With appropriate fanfare, NCTM declared the major task of the curriculum of the 80s to be the development at all levels of a true fundamental—problem-solving ability. The group then attempted to send this message to all segments of society by way of a free booklet entitled *An Agenda for Action* (1980).

looking around

Good mathematics instruction requires good thinking about mathematical objectives *and* about how children learn. A necessary part of this personal synthesis is the realization that there are several different types of basic mathematics learning, and that on these basics—facts, skills, and concepts—problem-solving ability is built. Because different methods should be used to teach each type, only when a mathematics learning is classified correctly can appropriate instruction be designed.

Facts are bits of information that, technically, do not need to be understood to be useful. Although it need not be confined to this level, $3+2=5$ can be taught as a fact, as can "A triangle has three sides." Although facts may be learned, repetition, immediate rewards for correct answers, and spaced review provide the external conditions necessary for the learning of facts. Application is facilitated, however, when one's store of information goes beyond well-memorized verbal strings.

Concepts, or mathematical ideas, must be taught in a way that understanding results. This depends on teaching in which a variety of examples are presented that vary in all nonessential attributes. Nonexamples must also be available for inspection, time for reflection must be built into instruction, and novel instances must be used in assessment. In concept teaching it is wise to begin with real objects, then move to pictures, and only when the children are able to work effectively at these levels move to symbols. Initial instruction into the meaning of *three,* for example, might begin with having the children form groups of three using many objects such as three beans, three clothespins, and three crayons. The next set of tasks would focus on identifying and constructing pictures of three objects. The final stage would be to introduce "3" and help the child accept this symbol as a shorthand for sets of three items. Planning instruction that has concept learning as its goal calls for careful assessment of the child's current cognitive level, the fostering of an inquiring nature, the imaginative choice of examples, and the presentation of varied tasks that require the application of the attained learnings.

Skills can run the gamut from almost totally physical to almost totally mental processes. Forming a "5" is an example of the former; adding two-digit numbers can be an example of the latter (it could also be taught as a rote sequence of steps). After correct models and initial instruction have been presented, monitored practice is a necessary step in instruction. Taking part in interesting opportunities to use the skill is the spoonful of sugar that makes this essential medicine go down. Patient acceptance of initial efforts keeps the task from being oppressive.

Attention to both *what* is taught and *how* it should be taught is important. It is hoped that in planning instruction you will consider the logical needs of the subject, the psychological needs of the students, and the mathematics children need now and later in the real world. When all these forces are considered in the development of mathematics curriculum, the chances are greatly increased that mathematics will be taught humanely and thoroughly and that in your classroom the long-awaited synthesis will be a reality. The payoff for you will be the knowledge that you have done your best to assist children in developing their own syntheses—solid foundations in the mathematics needed to solve problems involving number and measurement.

three

who are the children?

Although no classroom was ever comprised of children who were just alike, the range of physical and mental capacities of children in any given class has expanded enormously since the passage of a long-overdue bill requiring that all children and adolescents be given a free appropriate education. In the past, many children with special needs were not in school at all, were in an isolated setting within the public school, or were educated at and/or transported to special educational settings at their parents' expense. PL 94–142 was designed to remedy that situation and to provide the optimal learning environment for all children regardless of handicap.

the education of children with special needs

Popularly known as the mainstreaming act (although those words appear nowhere in the document), PL 94–142, the Education for All Handicapped Children Act of 1975, mandates a free and appropriate education in the least restrictive environment, a nondiscriminatory assessment, and educational due process for all children and youth. Because for many mildly handicapped children the "least restrictive environment" required by law is the ordinary classroom, at least for part of the school day, the heterogeneity of almost every classroom in the nation has been increased. For some part of their career, all early childhood teachers will probably have as pupils some mildly handicapped children. It is therefore important for all teachers to know the characteristics of the children they may find in their classrooms and the methods of instruction most likely to be beneficial and efficient.

Not until the late 1850s was attention given to children with learning problems in any positive way at all, and then it was only minimal. Until that time there were few techniques employed in reaching hard-to-reach children. Communication systems for blind or deaf children were not yet in widespread use. Only the crudest measures for assessing intellectual potential were available. The plethora of devices to aid the physically handicapped were not yet invented. "Acting out" behavior was more likely to be seen as a moral fault than as a condition needing professional attention. Even when techniques were developed, the education of handicapped children was the province of only specially trained teachers. Until the present decade, other teachers in the building might go for days without meeting or thinking about the educational needs of these school citizens. This is no longer the case.

Many of the first classes for special children were begun as experiments by concerned individuals, some of whom had personal or family reasons for becoming involved in the quest for better education of children with special needs. During the 1950s and 1960s parents became more assertive about the school's responsibility for properly educating handicapped children. As parent groups became more vocal, more children who deviated from the norm on physical, perceptual, mental, or behavioral dimensions began to attend public schools. Typically, the accommodations for these children were not ideal. The children might be assigned to a regular classroom with no assistance for the teacher and no modification of the curriculum or instructional procedures for the children. Another typical solution was the establishment of "opportunity rooms." Children who were placed in these rooms had very little, if any, contact with the others in the school, even in nonacademic settings such as lunch and assembly.

This special placement of children branded them as different in significant ways from "normal" children. That labeling became an issue for debate: Was it more harmful to label children and thus respond to individuals on the basis of their membership within a group, or was it better to ignore the differences and threat all children as nearly alike as possible and thus avoid class identification? The debate is not yet resolved, but PL 94–142 had demanded a middle ground.

Under the new legislation, each child must be regarded as an individual with special needs, and both the child's and the parents' rights are carefully guarded. Before a child can be tested for special placement, his or her parents must give informed consent; that is, parents must be notified why the tests are being done, and the proposed action must be communicated in a way that the parents will understand it. Placement must be based on more than one test and is not considered permanent, and testing must be done in language that the child understands. The child's records are open to the parents and to those they designate, and private assessment may be obtained by parents who wish it. Parents are to be involved in the planning of the child's individual educational program (IEP) and may reopen discussion at any stage if they are dissatisfied with it. Hearings on any part of the process must be conducted according to rules that ensure an impartial decision.

The children who fall under the Education for All Handicapped Children Act include those who are mentally retarded, deaf and hard of hearing, visually impaired, emotionally disturbed, learning disabled, orthopedically and otherwise health impaired, speech impaired, and those who belong to other categories determined by individual states affected by this act. Free appropriate education must be provided for all of these children who are between the ages of three and twenty-one, although it is not required before five or after eighteen if this is inconsistent with state law or practice or court orders (Schifani, Anderson, and Odle 1980). Because for many children the proper placement is an ordinary classroom with additional human or mechanical assistance, all those preparing to teach should be familiar with the educational and personal ramifications of such placements. In the course of a career, a primary or elementary teacher may have among his or her pupils many with special needs that must be considered in planning for mathematics instruction.

The rest of this chapter outlines some of the characteristics of those children most likely to be receiving regular or supplementary mathematics instruction from the regular classroom teacher. It is merely a brief introduction. Should you have a child with special needs in your classroom, it is your professional responsibility to learn all you can about the child's handicapping condition, both in general and as it relates to the young human being with whom you are establishing an ongoing relationship. Much of this information will be available from the special education teachers in your school or district. Especially when the child is placed in more than one setting, communication among the adults responsible for his or her educational progress is crucial. It is not always easy to arrange schedules and responsibilities that are convenient for all concerned. Working cooperatively with the other teachers is important in ensuring that the child will have the best possible school experience.

It may be necessary for you to take a leadership role in creating within your classroom a climate of acceptance and help for the special-needs child. Many children may harbor myths or have outdated information about the handicapping condition of a student with special needs. Some of their parents may also be concerned and may not understand the condition either. Perhaps you, the special education teachers, and the local administrators can use the establishment of a comfortable yet challenging atmosphere within your classroom as one of your first working tasks.

On the next few pages you will be reading about several types of disabling conditions. It is important to realize that the degree to which each is considered a handicap will depend heavily on the individual. Two children who are identical on paper may view themselves very differently and may come to your classroom with very different histories. Do not be overswayed by an IQ score or an audiologist's report. Treat each child as an individual worthy of your learning about on his or her own terms.

Finally, a word about the descriptors used for the various disabling conditions: It is difficult to find words and phrases that remain acceptable to everyone and that remain so over time. Especially with respect to the mentally retarded, labels that were once acceptable, such as *feebleminded*, are now considered abusive, unfeeling, or insulting. Of necessity in communication, descriptors must be used. Those employed here are those currently prevalent in the literature of special education.

the mentally retarded child

Mental retardation is a multifaceted condition that affects about 3 percent of the population. The majority of this 3 percent are mildly retarded. It is persons from this group whom you will most likely encounter as students in a "regular" classroom. One of the most widely accepted of the many definitions of this condition is that formulated by the American Association on Mental Deficiency:

> Mental retardation refers to significantly subaverage general intellectual functioning existing currently with deficits in adaptive behavior, and manifested during the developmental period (Laycock in Schifani, Anderson, and Odle 1980).

The term *adaptive behavior* refers to the individual's ability to meet the changing social and natural demands of the environment and is seen by Piaget and others as a hallmark of intelligence. An individual who cannot adapt is destined to be dependent or semidependent on others throughout his or her life.

The mentally retarded child who is mildly affected (sometimes termed *educable*) can usually progress in school mathematics through about the fifth-grade level. The time required for this level of achievement will be the entire thirteen-year schooling period, and even then some of the more advanced concepts such as long division, operations with fractions, percentage, and abstract problem solving may not be mastered. The moderately retarded (also known as *trainable*) individual may, at the end of his or her school career, be able to use the concepts usually associated with the second-grade curriculum. In Piaget's schema, the educable child will reach but not leave the concrete operational stage; the trainable child may not reach the concrete operational stage. Those who do not advance beyond the sensorimotor stage are termed severely and profoundly retarded, and they usually receive services outside the public school system.

Mentally retarded youngsters may have difficulty remembering material, transferring what has been learned to what is newly presented, and applying previous learnings in problem-solving situations, all of which affect the learning of mathematics. This is not to say that all mentally retarded children in the schools are alike; nothing could be further from the truth. Each child, retarded or not, is an individual with his or her own pattern of strengths and weaknesses. Like all children, the mentally retarded vary from each other in physical, social, and emotional maturity; in learning habits and motivation. It is the teacher's task to learn about each child in the classroom as thoroughly as possible and then use that knowledge in planning interesting, effective lessons.

As for all children, initial instruction should be very concrete for retarded children. In addition, the time spent at the concrete level should generally be much greater than for other children. All new learnings should be practiced for an extended period of time. In providing this repetition, it is essential that the materials and the method of instruction be varied, which means the teacher must learn many alternative strategies for teaching each concept and skill.

Working with the mentally retarded student who has difficulty in acquiring and retaining information will necessitate frequent well-structured reviews, especially if new material depends upon previously learned concepts, facts, and skills. These reviews need not be dull and should not be lengthy. Frequent focused drill in a variety of formats is most efficient. All children may occasionally have trouble relating what has been learned to a new learning task, but this difficulty is prevalent among the retarded. Making the new learning task as concrete as possible and highlighting the similarities between it and what has been previously mastered will help.

Retarded children frequently have difficulty generalizing from past experiences or developing efficient problem-solving strategies. Because these children often do not learn what is not specifically taught, teachers have to be aware that essential steps cannot be skipped or only casually mentioned. Systematic teaching is important, and generalizations may have to be "teased out" over an extended period of time. To promote error-free transfer of knowledge, it is crucial that practice on learned material be varied and that student work be quickly corrected and discussed with the child.

When it comes to learning mathematics, teachers can expect the retarded child to have more difficulty learning concepts than memorizing facts, more difficulty solving word problems than following step-by-step procedures, and more difficulty finding patterns than following specific directions. The teacher who carefully sequences instruction, is patient in its delivery, and employs a wide variety of alternative strategies is likely to help children—especially the mentally retarded—experience learning success.

Since the days of Itard, sensory stimulation has been a major instructional technique for helping the retarded individual acquire knowledge, and it is still a good one. Language development is important also. The *Workjobs II* kits (Baratta-Lorton 1979) are excellent providers of both kinds of experience. They are mathematically sound yet are so appealing they call out to be handled and talked about. The kits are appropriate for lessons dealing with the concept of number, addition and subtraction, or fractions, so children at many levels can use the same materials in different ways; therefore, the slower children in the class are not singled out in a derogatory manner. As the work of preparing the kits is time and cost effective, the construction of several kits is a very worthwhile endeavor for the classroom teacher.

With respect to curriculum for the retarded student, the best course is to opt for those learnings that have the highest probability of helping the child become an independent adult. For example, an independent person must be able to handle time and money. Because these are abstract topics, they will take a very long time to learn; instruction in them should begin early and build consistently throughout the student's school career. The "simple" act of making change requires subtraction (usually with regrouping) of multiplaced numbers—not an easy task. Planning for wise use of time may require adding and subtracting fractions—another notoriously difficult topic even for children who can progress at a normal rate through the school math program.

So that sufficient time is devoted to mathematics useful in daily life, some traditional topics may need to be cut. When you make that decision, choose for inclusion those topics most practical in adult life—measuring food for a recipe rather than memorizing tables of equivalents, understanding the decimal system rather than decoding Roman numerals, and learning to use a calculator rather than learning to do long division by hand.

the perceptually handicapped child

the visually handicapped child

Children who have total loss of vision are called blind. Those who retain some vision are called visually impaired. The term *visually handicapped* includes both categories.

Children who are visually handicapped have been placed in regular classroom settings longer than other handicapped children. Many of them are able to use large-print editions of the same books the other children use; some use Braille editions; some use a special machine called the Opticon, which translates regular print into tactile stimulation. Curriculum modifications are therefore usually less taxing on the teacher than instructional modifications.

As for all children with special needs, the visually handicapped should be placed in the least restrictive environment. For some this may be a regular classroom with some special equipment or some occasional assistance by an aide or itinerant teacher. Others may be placed in a regular classroom for much of the day but may visit a resource room for scheduled instructional periods. Still others may have primary placement in a self-contained classroom or in a residential center. Also, as for all children covered under PL 94–142, there may be more than one handicap to consider in designing instruction. A child may be both blind and deaf, for example, or blind and orthopedically handicapped. Often one of the conditions is the primary determiner of placement, although all professionals realize that each handicap affects performance. The provider of instruction must be alert to the ramifications of multiple disabilities and sometimes must risk trying new instructional methods uniquely suited to an individual child.

About 75 percent of blind children were born that way or lost their sight before age one (Marin and Martinez in Schifani, Anderson, and Odle 1980). Visual stimulation, a primary learning modality for the young child, has thus been denied them. For sighted persons, visual input helps organize isolated bits of data and aids the development of interpersonal relations. Primary teachers must emphasize both of these areas for children without sight. Extensive hands-on experiences are essential, as is careful utilization of the child's remaining senses. Because the necessary continual verbal flow may be impossible for the teacher with twenty-five to thirty other children to help, it would be wise to enlist the help of the blind child's peers. Even with peer tutors, however, continuing supervision by the teacher is not optional; the child will require much corrected practice and emotional support.

Active exploration of the environment is a good learning strategy for all young people. It is especially important for the visually handicapped child. If a child has been overprotected, he or she may need special coaxing to explore. Recognizing the importance of this activity, teachers should provide enticing experiences that will help the child create a solid cognitive map of the universe.

The attitude of the classroom teacher towards the visually handicapped child (as for any child) will in large part determine the quality of life in that classroom for that child. If the teacher is calmly accepting of individual differences, the class will be apt to follow that model. If the teacher is rejecting or oversolicitous, the class will follow suit. Although the visually handicapped child may require your shortening some seatwork assignments, that child, like every other, should be held responsible for doing acceptable individual work and taking part in class projects. The provision of tape-recorded lessons, carefully chosen counters, Braille or large-print textbooks, talking calculators, and tactile tape measures and clocks will help the visually handicapped child be a contributing, learning member of the mathematics group.

the hearing-handicapped child

Deaf and hard-of-hearing children must trudge a long and laborious path before language facility is theirs. The greater and earlier the hearing loss, the more scholastic and interpersonal development is bound to suffer (Clarke and Leslie in Schifani, Anderson, and Odle 1980). Although recent technology has greatly aided many hearing-handicapped children, artificial aids only begin to compensate for the lack of normal hearing. In addition, within the field of special education there is controversy over which communication system is best. Generally, the best thinking on the subject points to a multisensory or total communication approach.

It is in many ways difficult to get an accurate assessment of the intellectual potential of the hearing-handicapped child. Well-accepted tests were standardized on a hearing population, and some items may not be valid for deaf or hard-of-hearing children. Normally, however, the hearing-impaired or deaf child progresses through the math curriculum at a slower rate than the hearing child of approximately equal ability. The highly verbal nature of the classroom helps explain this fact. Even in special settings for the hearing impaired, progress in mathematics curriculum is often impeded, though not so badly as progress in reading and language arts.

Emotional problems for hearing-handicapped children, as for children with other disabling conditions, are not rare. Frustration often explodes into anger or implodes into sadness or depression. Social support may be difficult for children to gauge when communication is uncomfortable, as it often is between a young deaf child and his or her hearing peers or teachers. The level of hearing loss, the child's social history, and personal traits should all be taken into consideration when the least restrictive environment for that child is chosen or reassessed.

Learning tasks that are the most challenging for the hearing-handicapped child are, of course, those with the highest verbal component. You must present material in such a way that residual hearing is maximally utilized and that tactile and visual stimuli are very obvious at first. Many of the techniques presented in the following chapters for use with hearing-intact children will be equally successful with hearing-handicapped children. Devices that have built-in evaluative features such as Stern number pattern boards and Cuisenaire rods are particularly appropriate.

Hearing-handicapped children, like visually handicapped children, vary greatly as a group in their ability to learn, remember, and apply mathematics facts, concepts, and skills. Their rate of assignment completion is apt to be slowed because of the greater difficulty in receiving and/or decoding input, which does not mean they cannot learn well. As always, carefully diagnosing the child's current level of achievement, planning on the basis of the diagnosis, and delivering instruction in a supportive atmosphere are the surest steps to success.

the learning-disabled child

A child who has a specific learning disability can be baffling to teachers and parents. He or she (a far greater proportion of boys than girls are learning disabled) *seems* capable of doing good work and indeed may be highly verbal but may seem continually distracted, sloppy in work habits, and forgetful. If such a child's academic performance is significantly below his or her evaluated potential, if vision and hearing screening have shown there is no problem, if severe motor and emotional problems have been ruled out, then the child may well be learning disabled and should be referred for further testing.

Coined in the late 1950s, "learning disabled" is one of the newest labels for children. The condition is believed to affect about 3 percent of the population, but estimates vary widely. Children who are learning disabled may perform well in some areas and poorly in others. The affected areas may be language related (such as reading) or not (such as mathematics or handwriting). To be considered learning-disability related, poor performance in these areas must not be attributable to emotional disturbance, visual or auditory handicaps, mental or motor handicaps, or environmental disadvantage. In short, the disability must be mysterious in origin. Because the child with learning disabilities is in many ways like an immature child, early diagnosis is often quite difficult.

The child who is learning disabled frequently seems unable to manage time or space. His or her math examples may be crowded into one corner of a paper or sprawled all over it in apparently random order. Reversals (such as 19 for 91) may be common, and copying mistakes may abound. Size and shape comparisons may be poorly made despite repeated instruction. Even the most concentrated effort may produce a messy paper—perhaps complete with rips and tear stains.

Many of the assumptions teachers make about children in general cannot be made about the learning-disabled child. For example, teachers assume students can:

Sit quietly and listen carefully to an academic presentation.

Complete independent seatwork and homework.

Coordinate eye and hand motion to manipulate objects smoothly.

Copy material correctly and organize their papers into readable and workable formats.

Discriminate between right and left.

Recall and write mathematical symbols.

Remember the sequence of steps required for numeral processing.

Memorize basic facts for addition and subtraction.

Learn and use correctly mathematical terminology and symbols.

(Moyer and Moyer 1978)

Any or all of these may be invalid assumptions for a given learning-disabled child.

Many learning-disabled children need more than time to deal with their memory deficits, eye-hand coordination problems, and spatial relationships difficulties. They need the help of a concerned, trained specialist as well as a concern, informed classroom teacher. The possible causes of the condition are many and probably cannot be undone. Helping the child reach his or her potential level of achievement and be self-accepting is usually more beneficial than an anguished search for the cause of the condition. Specialists in learning disabilities can be a great resource for the classroom teacher who has a mainstreamed child with specific learning disabilities.

When one prepares work for such a child, a quick review is in order of those factors just listed that are relevant to that particular child. Sometimes a simple technique such as writing exercises on individual cards rather than in a group on a ditto sheet may help. Color cuing (begin at green, stop at red) is also often useful. The answers to problems may be read into a tape recorder for the child who does not write well, or the problems themselves may be taped for the child who can do the math but can't read. The teacher who has a learning-disabled student must truly focus on that individual's needs if his or her weaknesses are to be coped with and his or her strengths developed.

the orthopedically handicapped child and the health-impaired child

Many children who previously received their only instruction from homebound tutors or who were placed in residential settings are now found in the "ordinary" classroom. Some of these children have an external sign of their handicap (crutches, braces, wheelchairs); others have speech or motor patterns that are apparent; some have invisible drains on their strength and vitality.

As can be expected, children with health problems run the gamut on every possible dimension—academic potential, social skills, emotional stability, and interest in school tasks. Each child must be carefully diagnosed and an IEP (Individual Education Plan) drawn up that takes into consideration the strengths and weaknesses and long-range prognosis for the child.

Some children with good academic potential are hampered because of necessary frequent absences. Perhaps you could implement a buddy system to assist the child in catching up. Other children take medication or have symptoms that sporadically or regularly interrupt their ability to concentrate. Both they and their parents will appreciate your cooperation during times of stress.

Those who have orthopedic problems often have appliances that help them sit or stand comfortably and thus help preserve energy that can be used for intellectual tasks. A discussion with a student's parents about how the apparatus functions and how the classroom might be made more comfortable will help alleviate your concerns about how to provide a good physical environment for the child. Children who have difficulty controlling hand and arm motions may need special counters. Counters are so important to the learning of mathematics that it is worth considerable trouble to find appropriate ones. Again, talking to the parents may help.

If your responsibility for the health condition of any of your students is unclear to you, be sure to get the necessary information. If the health condition of any of your students is unsettling to you, be sure to talk to someone. Your unease, repugnance, or drawing away could be very harmful to the student and will surely prevent good teacher-student interaction.

the emotionally handicapped child

Children who are severely emotionally handicapped will probably find a self-contained classroom with a specially trained teacher the least restrictive environment. Less severely handicapped children may be able to cope in a regular classroom setting with occasional visits to a resource room.

Because mathematics is a subject that tends to raise tensions, even for children on an even emotional keel, teachers should be very careful to maintain a supportive climate when mathematics learning is expected. The subject is a very abstract and cumulative one and can be deeply distressing to those who are afraid to risk being wrong. Allowing students plenty of time to think, sending a strong message that mistakes are natural and can be learned from, and providing interesting learning tasks are principles of good teaching that should be underlined when the learners have emotional problems.

the speech-impaired child

Usually speech impairment has little effect on mathematical progress if alternatives to oral responses are given to the child not yet ready for public performance. For the child with difficulties in the production of oral language, an early and thorough diagnosis is essential lest emotional problems become a confounding factor.

the gifted child

Children gifted in mathematics are usually fairly easy to identify in a classroom in which choice of activity is encouraged and individual accomplishment applauded. Gifted children usually show a strong interest in the processes of mathematics and work independently on mathematical projects. They make quick and usually accurate generalizations, become deeply absorbed in mathematical tasks, ask many "what would happen if . . ." questions, and accept challenges joyfully.

The objectives of an early childhood program for such children should be to develop the students' ability to produce multiple solutions for various tasks, ask questions that lead to independent exploration, synthesize ideas in creative ways, encourage them to work with others as well as alone, and teach them to view themselves as competent and creative problem solvers. Some teachers, not perceiving themselves as gifted in mathematics, worry that even at the early childhood level they will be unable to provide such a program. They should be comforted to know that successful teachers of the gifted are apt to be those who love and are excited by their jobs, who are orderly and businesslike but imaginative in their approach to teaching, and who are interested in a wide variety of areas. One of the most important qualities of a teacher of the gifted is the ability to accept individual differences and deviations from the norm. Another is to glory in new learning—your own and other people's.

Teaching the gifted is not all a bed of roses. These children can be demanding, argumentative, resistant to following directions, and stubborn. They can also be eager learners, alert, friendly, and awe inspiring. How specifically can a teacher help the child gifted in mathematics? Here are a few suggestions:

Support unusual approaches to problems.

Reinforce looking for "other ways."

Help students analyze their errors.

Provide computational practice in moderate (not excessive) amounts.

Adapt practice exercises to student interests when possible.

Provide resource materials from many subject areas and from the real world for creating problem-solving materials.

Allow choice whenever possible.

Help children develop skill in questioning and research techniques including finding resources, taking notes, organizing findings, and preparing synthesis of findings.

Stress searching for relationships and generalizations.

Emphasize the process over the product in most assignments.

Three resources for the gifted at the primary level are especially excellent. *Mathematics Their Way* (1976) and *Workjobs II* (1979), both by Mary Baratta-Lorton, give teachers suggestions and reproducible worksheets for unusual activities for use with gifted children, and *Drill and Practice at the Problem-Solving Level* (1974) by Robert Wirtz is a large set of reproducible worksheets that provides exactly what the title says.

It seems like quite a challenge, doesn't it? All these young children looking to you to help them learn so many things. But for the teacher who is prepared, it is a joyous, exhilarating challenge. I hope it will be that for you.

four

classification:
the first component

A basic prenumber activity is classification. It involves choosing an attribute such as blueness and separating objects into sets according to the chosen criteria. This ability is prerequisite to a child's ability to form sets using some more abstract criteria and to an understanding of number (Brearley et al. 1970). Classification lays the groundwork for consideration of relationships among elements. It is the earliest stage of logical thinking and the foundation for an understanding of class inclusion and hierarchical classification. It deserves a place in the mathematics program of all young children.

Inhelder and Piaget (1958) hypothesize that classification ability proceeds by a sequence of partially ordered tasks:

1. Grouping two objects that look alike in some way.
2. Grouping more than two objects.
3. Grouping all the objects of a set.
4. Sorting by attributes more permanent than physical proximity.

Research by Kofsky (1966) confirmed this hierarchy. She found 90 percent and 81 percent of the four-year-olds tested able to do tasks 1 and 2 respectively, and the tested five-year-olds were able to do task 3.

classification materials

Classification material can be purchased from commercial suppliers or gathered from garage sales and discount stores. Commercial sets, called attribute or logic blocks, are available from companies such as those listed in Appendix B. An attribute set usually consists of plastic or wooden pieces in several shapes, sizes, and colors. Attributes such as thickness or texture may also be included. A less abstract type of commercial set is composed of stylized figures of animals, trees, or houses in several colors, sizes, or styles.

Environmental materials that lend themselves easily to classification are buttons, seashells, jars of mixed macaroni and/or beans, old keys, plastic soldiers or trucks, leaves, tiles, play money, doll clothing, nails and screws, bottle tops, plastic picnic utensils, pictures cut from magazines, beads, pattern blocks, fabric or wallpaper squares, plastic toy dishes, unshelled mixed nuts, and boxes of broken and whole crayons or pencils. Teachers need not collect all these themselves. A request sent home with the children for donated material will elicit more than enough "stuff." ("Stuff" is a shorthand word for everyday materials used in mathematics instruction.)

classification tasks

When they have a collection of items, most children sort them instinctively. They put the red ones here and all the rest there, all the big ones in one box and all the small ones in another, or the squares in one pile and the circles in another. They eat the potatoes in the stew first and leave the carrots until last. Children of kindergarten age usually are able to sort first by color and shape and later by size (Lee 1965). Presented with a set of objects classifiable in several ways, young children can classify according to only one dimension at a time. Indeed they initially will have trouble doing even that. They may instead start by making sets of red and not red, and then they may switch to making sets of big and little.

Classification activities lead a child to ponder at an intuitive level such mathematical notions as set inclusion, intersection, and the null set. It can also lead to interesting discussions that build a vocabulary of both mathematical and nonmathematical words.

As a first step to classifying, children must be able to discern differences among objects. A popular song from "Sesame Street," "One of These Things Is Not Like the Others", provides practice in this skill. An example: Given a set containing a knife, a fork, a spoon, and a toy car, the children are asked to decide which one doesn't belong. After the song has been sung, the teacher can choose one child to tell which object doesn't belong and why. In this case the car may be designated because all the rest are eating utensils. Sometimes a different item or reason than that the teacher had in mind is offered. If it makes sense, it should be accepted. The object of the activity is to discern differences—not to read the teacher's mind.

The Hap Palmer song "Just Like Yours" from his record *Math Readiness Vocabulary and Concepts* (1972) provides another classification activity. Give each child one piece from an attribute set, and have the children scatter around the room. Explain that they are to hold the shapes high in the air and sway the shapes in time to the music.

Just Like Yours

First verse:
Find someone who has a shape that's just like yours
Find someone who's holding the same shape
Find someone who has a shape that's just like yours
Find someone who's holding the same shape.

Second verse:
Now trade shapes with the person you found
So everyone is holding a different shape
Now trade shapes with the person you found
So everyone is holding a different shape.

Third verse:
Find someone who has a shape that's not like yours
Find someone who's holding a different shape
Find someone who has a shape that's not like yours
Find someone who's holding a different shape.

Fourth verse:
Find someone who has a shape that's just like yours
Find someone who's holding the same shape
Find someone who has a shape that's just like yours
Find someone who's holding the same shape.

Another classification activity makes use of a sorting or feely box (Figure 4–1, page 41). To make the latter, cut a round hole in each end of a shoebox. To one end attach a sock; the other end is for the insertion of material to be felt. Glue two circles of yarn onto the bottom, inside the box. For beginners the circles should look like this:

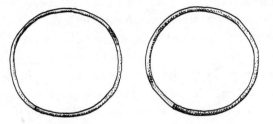

For more advanced students they would look like this:

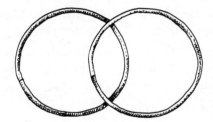

The child to be the "feeler" sticks one hand through the sock into the box. One at a time, the teacher hands the child objects to be put into previously agreed-on sets—rough and smooth, for example, or heavy and light. When all the objects have been sorted, the teacher lifts the top to see how each item was classified, and the children can discuss why each was classified as it was. Once they learn the procedure, children can play this game in pairs. They seldom tire of it, as new objects can be added at any time. Reliance on the sense of touch provides additional novelty.

If your students enjoy cut-and-paste activities, they may enjoy making sets from magazine pictures. Many kindergarten and first-grade classes study the four seasons, the four food groups, or the five senses in science. A popular activity is to glue pictures showing examples of each onto a divided paper plate or onto separate pieces of paper for a booklet. This is a classification activity, though it is seldom thought of in that way. A sorting box such as is shown in Figure 4–1 is an advanced approach to this task.

Classification permits creative responses and helps refine guessing strategies. If each student is given a handful of shells and asked to put them into two piles so that all the shells in one pile are alike in some way and all the shells in the other pile are alike in some way, so that all the shells are used up, some interesting groupings are bound to happen. Once

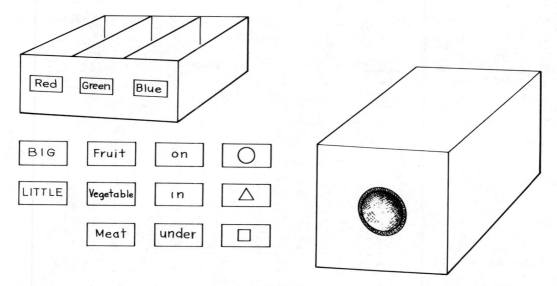

Figure 4–1   *A Feely Box and a Teacher-Made Sorting Box with Several Sets of Labels*

every shell has been classified, each child should choose a partner and then guess how the other classified. Now have each child classify the same shells in a different way. Repeat the guessing activity. Repeat the whole activity at least one more time.

Bottle tops, buttons, tiles, and keys also make especially versatile materials. Teachers who cannot collect their own shells may be able to buy them inexpensively in bulk at an import or a craft shop. Although you can acquire commercially made classification materials or use "stuff," you can also make your own set of attribute pieces. The set should consist of several different shapes in different sizes, colors, and/or textures. Some materials you might want to consider, depending on your resources, are wallpaper, contact-papered cardboard, painted wood, or colored Styrofoam. An eighteen-piece set with three shapes, three patterns, and two sizes is shown in Figure 4–2, page 42. For use on the overhead projector, sets in four shapes, two sizes, and with one, two, or no holes punched in each object are easy to construct. Sorting can be done into bags, onto two different paper plates, or just into piles.

One activity that uses an attribute set in a challenging way is the difference train. Pass one piece from the set to each person and then announce, "We are going to make a one-difference train." Choose any

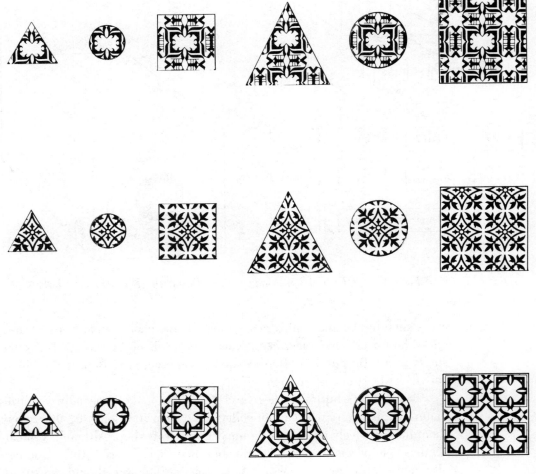

Figure 4—2   *A Wallpaper Attribute Set*

piece to start with, and ask everyone who has a piece different in *only one way* from that piece to raise it in the air. Choose one child to join you in making a train. Ask that child to repeat the question, "Who has a piece different from this in only one way?" The game continues until all the pieces are used or an impasse is reached. Two-difference trains can also be made and, if the set has four attributes, three-difference trains can be made. The latter are very challenging. A variation of this whole-class activity is to have groups of five or six students construct trains on a tabletop from a part of the set. Much good discussion will ensue.

ESS, one of the science curricula that incorporates child-centered science instruction, uses classification activities in a unit on logic. One such creative activity is the use of creature cards. Can you figure out this adaptation of the ESS creature cards?

All of these are Mibecks: None of these are Mibecks:

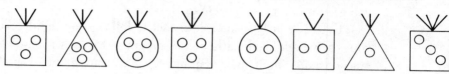

Which of these are Mibecks?

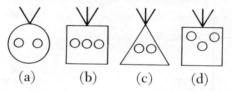

(a)   (b)   (c)   (d)

If you answered (b) and (d), you met the challenge. Congratulations! (A Mibeck has three eyes *and* three hairs.)

Classification can form the basis for interesting activities such as the challenging game "Make a Matrix."

The Setup:

1.   Make a 4″ x 4″ square grid, each square of which will hold an attribute piece.
2.   Each of two players will have half the pieces of a thirty-two piece set.
3.   Player A goes first.

The Play:

1.   Player A places one piece on the grid.
2.   Player B places a piece next to the first piece. If it is to the right or left, the new piece must differ from the first piece in *one* way; if placed above or below the first piece, the new piece must differ in *two* ways.
3.   Player A places a piece next, following the horizontal: one difference; vertical: two difference rule.
4.   A player who cannot place a piece loses that turn.
5.   The first player to be rid of all his or her pieces wins.

Variations:

1.   Try a solitaire version.
2.   Make another playing board in the form of an H with two columns on the uprights and one across as the horizontal bar.

Classification, which enables children to generate and impose a logical structure on the world (Kamii 1972, 109), is also the first step to graphing. It is hard to imagine an activity that captures the interest of children, builds language skills, leads to sophisticated mathematical activities, and is adaptable to a wide range of ability better than graphing. And before one can graph, one must be able to classify.

Even if you have no role model to follow, do include classification in your early childhood mathematics program. Piaget wrote, "The simultaneous construction of the groupings of classification and of qualitative seriation means the advent of the system of numbers (1950, 143)." His words are a valuable guide to one who would construct a mathematics program for young children that has as its objective the facilitation of the development of a solid concept of number.

five

seriation:

the second component

Both classification and seriation are important to the development of the concept of number. The ability to place objects in order according to a given or chosen criterion such as length, width, height, weight, diameter, or tone is a necessary prerequisite to dealing with the more abstract ordering of numbers and to thinking in terms of relations. Seriation provides a foundation for mathematics reasoning (Elkind 1974). "The long-term goals in classification and seriation are not to enable children to make little matrices and arrange little graduated sticks but to use the *process* of classification and seriation to isolate relevant variables and to generate and test hypotheses in dealing with the real world (Kamii 1972, 104)."

seriation materials and tasks

Four-year-olds spontaneously seriate (Kamii and DeVries 1976), and they easily place in order three sticks of varying length. Seriating a set of ten sticks requires a much higher level of skill. Children will develop this skill as they practice it in a variety of forms. Some of the many things that can be placed in order are cylinders (tin cans or painted paper towel rolls) of graduated height; metric weights; nesting boxes; identical soda bottles filled with various amounts of water; sealed matchboxes containing different amounts of rice or sand; clay balls rolled to different sizes; nails; commercial mathematics materials such as Montessori red rods, Stern blocks, or Cuisenaire rods; seashells; pictures of leaves (or actual leaves); books, children's clothing; strips of graph paper; chalk; rubber bands; paint chips (ordered by depth of hue); macaroni elbows or shells; jar tops; buttons; paperclips; same-width ribbons cut to various lengths; or same-length ribbons of various widths. Figure 5–1 shows two such orderings.

Double seriation is even more challenging. Nuts and bolts, jars and jar lids, shoes and feet—all these pairs require the ordering of each set singly, then the pairing of the smallest from each set together, then the next smallest, and so on (Figure 5–2). Providing experience in ordering with environmental and structural materials paves the way for correlating numeral names with numeral forms and for learning the sequence of the counting numbers. Experience with ordering need not be restricted to mathematically related material, however. Children enjoy sequencing pictures that tell a story. Some cartoon strips lend themselves nicely to this activity. Find a few that do, laminate each strip, cut the frames apart, and leave the pictures on a table for the children to discover. It is easy to overlook the fact that such activities provide mathematical as well as language arts experiences.

Figure 5–1   *An Ordering of Ribbons by Length and of Cans by Height*

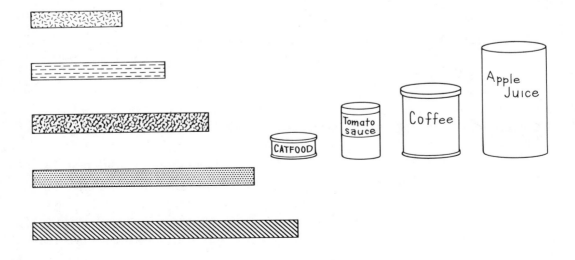

Seriation is important for the establishment of a complete concept of number. Number can be considered to have two "faces"—a discrete face and a continuous face. Counting out beans or shells gives children a way to experience discrete number meaning; seriating proportional rods gives children a way to experience continuous number meaning. Before children can have a strong sense of number, both of these meanings must be established, for both are used in more advanced work.

A word of caution: It may seem like a good idea to ask the class to seriate itself by height. This is a *very* difficult task for several reasons. First, children cannot see what they are doing while they participate in the activity. Second, there are many "items" to seriate. Thirdly, the differences in height are sometimes minimal. Fourth, the heights vary as children stand up tall, stretch their necks, or shift their weight from one foot to the other. This formidable task can be made easier if ribbons are cut to each person's height and the *ribbons* seriated. Have small groups seriate the ribbons before you extend the task to the whole group.

The inclusion of seriation activities in the early childhood curriculum will engage students with the processes of thinking, processes that are important in not only mathematical learning but also in the learning of science and social studies. Children who seriate and classify will be exploring similarities and differences, deciding which features of a situation are critical, making sense out of ambiguous situations, and responding in varied and novel ways to posed problems. According to Hofstadter (1979), these are the essential abilities of an intelligent person.

Figure 5–2   *A Double Ordering of Cookie Cutters and Playdough Cookies*

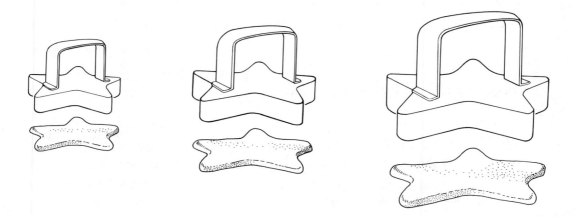

six

patterning:
going a step beyond

Uhr (1973) has declared that the whole purpose of sense perception is the recognition of patterns. Pattern recognition refers to the identification of a repetitive stimulus presented to a sense-perceiving organ. It is one thing to *see* and another to *perceive* a pattern. It is yet another thing to be able to identify and extend a pattern. Although perception has a neurological base, there is more to perception than the simple reception of stimuli. Receiving data from the world in terms of visual and auditory input is a necessary but not sufficient condition for understanding it. The sense organ impression is merely the raw material that the child uses to draw inferences, solve problems, and respond appropriately to the external world.

a theoretical point of view

Intelligence, Piaget said (1950, 167), is "a structuring which imposes certain patterns on the interaction between the subject or subjects and near or distant objects." Producing or discovering a pattern requires the noticing of similarities and differences and of differentiating between essential and nonessential features among a group of elements. Therefore, pattern recognition and generation is a hallmark of both human and artificial intelligence (Uhr 1973, 189).

Patterns abound in mathematics. Indeed, Usiskin (1979) goes so far as to say that algebra is the study of number patterns and geometry is the study of visual patterns. Moreover, because it is a sequential ordering of events, patterning lays the foundation for a later understanding of abstract temporal and spatial regularities in other disciplines.

Pattern perception involves abstraction, an important mental ability. "To make the abstraction, the subject must find the rules of relations or algorithms that generate a diverse array of objects from a few parental instances" (Kolers 1968, 50). Investigators of patterning among children and adults have found consistent age and mental ability differences but no consistent sex differences. Older and brighter children do better on all patterning tasks. Boys and girls do equally well on this problem-solving skill (Burton 1973). Engaging students in a search for patterns is both a pedagogically rewarding occupation and a good preparation for later mathematical development. There are a myriad of patterns in mathematics. Noticing them not only makes the learning of mathematics more solid but also fosters creativity and makes mathematics learning enjoyable (McKillip 1970).

As a type of perceptual schematization (Elkind 1974), patterns may be presented to the eye or the ear. They are less commonly presented in a motor modality, though this is also possible. They may be simple or complex. The ability to copy, identify, and extend patterns develops in that order and increases with mental age. More mature children can also translate and extrapolate patterns. Even four-year-olds can copy an uncomplicated AB pattern; extending a more complicated ABA pattern can challenge even the bright first grader.

types of patterns

Just what is an AB pattern? It is the repetition of two elements in alternating form as in round button, square button, round button, square button; or stand, sit, stand, sit; or do, mi, do, mi, do, mi. Other simple patterns appropriate for work with young children are ABC, AABB, ABCD, and ABA. The last is a little more difficult; there is little difference in difficulty between the other patterns mentioned.

Patterns are most commonly presented to young children using real objects, pictures, or symbols. They can be presented equally well using claps, drum beats, sung notes, or animal noises. It is also possible to present patterned sequences of motor activity—touch your shoulders, touch your knees, touch your shoulders, touch your knees. Many songs are accompanied by motor patterns (Do you know the old favorite "A-oonie-woonie-cowar oonie"?). And, of course, all basic ballroom dance steps (1, 2, 3, slide, 1, 2, 3, slide) and most folk dances consist of repeating patterns.

patterning activities

It is unfortunate that patterning activities are so rarely a significant part of the early childhood program, because the ability to recognize patterns has a profound effect on a child's mathematical development. The use of patterning activities will enrich the curriculum and give the children a chance to generate unique creations. Encouraging a variety of responses discourages the all-too-common belief that in mathematics there is only one right answer. Here are a few ideas for patterning, using an AAB pattern as the repeating element or repetend.

1.   Clap your hands twice, then snap once. Repeat several times. Ask the children to join in as they recognize the rhythm (Baratta-Lorton 1976).

2.   Ask children to translate a clapping pattern into body movements (touch knees, touch knees, turn around, touch knees, touch knees, turn around).

3.   During physical education, encourage patterns in body movements (jump, jump, hop, jump, jump, hop).

4.   Place children in a row to make a pattern (first and second children stand, third child sits, fourth and fifth children stand, sixth child sits) [Baratta-Lorton 1976].

5.   Ask children to reproduce with buttons a pattern they see or hear (white, white, black, white, white, black).

6.   Have children string wooden beads or colored macaroni for a necklace (yellow, yellow, green, yellow, yellow, green).

7.   Supply children with rubber stamps and several stamp pads in different colors.

8.   Link interlocking paper circles in two different colors or two sizes of paperclips to form a long chain (red, red, blue, red, red, blue).

9.   During art, ask children to describe patterned fabric or wallpaper (red stripe, red stripe, blue stripe, red stripe, red stripe, blue stripe).

10.   After each child has used crayoned x's to make a pattern (brown, brown, blue, brown, brown, blue), have a friend translate the pattern into other colors (green, green, black, green, green, black) or into other symbols.

Although all the patterns in these examples are of the AAB type, other types should be used as well. In fact, it is preferable that many repetends be used. Because patterning is a problem-solving activity, the response should not be immediately evident to the child. Among the variables that the teacher can take into account when preparing patterning activities are the repetend form (AAB in the previous examples); the sense organ engaged (the eye, ear, skin, muscles); the way the pattern is presented (pictures, symbols, real objects); and the response requested (identify, copy, extend, translate, extrapolate). In addition, because anything that can be classified can be patterned, the variety of materials that can be used is practically limitless.

Patterns also come in two dimensions: fabric, tiling, wrapping paper and wallpaper are examples. Activities such as number 9 in the previous list can be extended, as actual wallpapering or tiling is extended, to fill a plane or to construct symmetric design in two dimensions.

An especially delightful plane-filling activity suggested by Baratta-Lorton (1976) involves each child writing his or her name in several square grids (Figure 6–1, page 52). The activity could be adopted to providing spelling practice as the word is written over and over. Once each square is filled, each child colors the first letter of the name each time it appears *as the first letter*. When all have finished, the group members can compare sheets and look for the patterns generated.

why patterning?

Patterning lays a solid foundation for later mathematical development. Some of later topics which depend on an ability to discover and use patterns are multiplication, the base-10 numeration system, and sequences and series. Although at first glance the relationship between these more advanced mathematical topics and alternating colored beads on a string or snapping paperclips together according to a set pattern scheme is obscure, it is potent. Those whose only school experiences with mathematics were of the no-nonsense, pencil-and-paper variety may doubt the power of these seemingly irrelevant tasks. Please be assured, however, that patterning is the basis of not only mathematics but also of many other areas of education. It is a high-level mental process, the development of which is well worth the time and effort of the early childhood educator.

Figure 6—1   *Partially Completed Name Pattern Sheet*

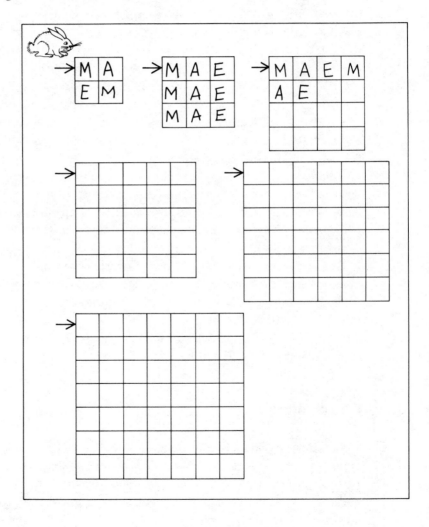

seven

describing relationships

in the beginning

Many relationships, including "is the same color as," "belongs to," "is wearing," and "is taller than," are of interest to young children. Sorting objects into sets having a common property, as in classification, or making graphs are two ways students can communicate the relationships they discover. The Nuffield Mathematics Guide *Mathematics Begins* (1972) is an excellent source for such activities. Like all the other Nuffield guides, this one emphasizes reporting of the data in a variety of ways. Suggested ways include:

1. Putting objects in a hoop and dividing the sets with a stick (fruit here, vegetables here).
2. Drawing pictures of the objects on either side of a line.

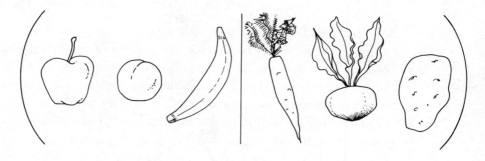

3.   Recording the objects by names in columns.

Fruit   Vegetable
_____

apple   carrot
peach   beet
banana   potato

4.   Writing the name of the objects on cards and arranging the cards in the form of a vertical bar graph.

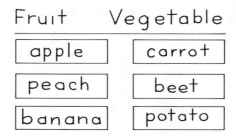

5.   Drawing arrows for each object to the appropriate classification.

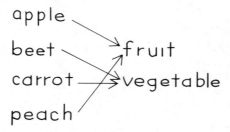

6.   Using a formal notation such as (apple, fruit); (carrot, vegetable).

Becoming aware of nonmathematical relationships such as "is the same color as" and "is the brother of" will lead to an awareness of mathematical relationships such as "has as many as," "is one more than," or "is longer than." The first is basic to an understanding of equality, the second to an understanding of counting, and the third to an understanding of linear measurement. In addition, the concept of one-to-one correspondence flows directly from "has as many as" a natural relationship for children who want one cookie for each hand.

equivalence relationships

Relationships that conform to a certain set of conditions are called equivalence relationships. It is this type which is the most useful to the future mathematical development of children. The three properties of an equivalence relationship R are:

Reflexive: $a\,R\,a$
Symmetric: If $a\,R\,b$, then $b\,R\,a$.
Transitive: If $a\,R\,b$ and $b\,R\,c$, then $a\,R\,c$.

In English, the reflexive property states that the object has the relation under question to itself. The symmetric property states that if an object has some relation to a second object, the second object has that relationship to the first. The transitive property states that if a has some relationship to b, and b has that same relationship to c, then a has that relationship to c.

Not all relationships are equivalence relationships. Whether or not a relationship is an equivalence relationship can be easily determined by testing each property in turn. Let us test "is a sister of," for example.

Reflexive: Is Cathy the sister of Cathy? No.

This statement is not true; therefore, "is the sister of" is not an equivalence relationship. Let's try "is the same height as."

Reflexive: Is it true that Jim is the same height as Jim? Yes.
Symmetric: Is it true that if Jim is the same height as Polly, Polly is the same height as Jim? Yes.
Transitive: Is it true that if Marcee is the same height as Jim and Jim is the same height as Polly, then Marcee is the same height as Polly? Yes.

All the statements are true; therefore, "is the same height as" is an equivalence relationship. Let's test that relationship in a more abstract form.

Reflexive: Is it true that a line segment is as long as itself? Yes.
Symmetric: Is it true that if line segment A is as long as line segment B, then line segment B is as long as line segment A? Yes.

Transitive: Is it true that if line segment A is as long as line
                   segment B and line segment B is as long as line
                   segment C, then line segment A is as long as line
                   segment C? Yes.

All the statements are true; therefore, "is the same length as" is an equivalence relationship.

It is not important—and *not* recommended—that children use these terms, but it *is* important that they grasp the underlying concepts and test their understanding of relationships in novel situations. Such practice will later come in handy in "guess my rule" games when, given pairs (3, 5), (2, 4), (5, 7), children supply new ordered pairs.

A very special set of relationships has the transitive but *not* the reflexive property or the symmetric property: seriation. Called an ordering relation, you will recall that seriation is one of the major concepts underlying number. When a child can form classes and order series, the concrete operational stage begins (Beard 1969). The teacher cannot lecture or argue the child into developing logical thinking ability. He or she can provide the opportunity for the child to seriate and classify a variety of objects and to discuss relationships among them.

eight

rote counting

From the time a child is about three, adults frequently ask, "How high can you count?" At first, counting means simply reciting the names of the whole numbers in their proper order, saying every number only once and not skipping over any. To help the child develop this ability, parents often say the first few number names slowly and ask the child to repeat them. "Come on, count for Daddy. Say 'one, two, three . . .'" When the child pauses, the parent typically says, "And what comes next?" The child who can't remember is usually reminded of the answer and asked to repeat the sequence.

the size of the task

Because the child is being asked to memorize a fairly large string of unrelated nonsense sounds, it usually takes many practice sessions before the ability to count to ten is established. (The sounds we make to tell "how many" are purely a cultural convention and have no meaning in themselves.) These practice sessions are usually enjoyable for both parent and child because two individuals who care for each other are cooperating in a joint enterprise. Counting aloud has also become a standard feature in television programs such as "Sesame Street." As a result of hours watching TV, many children come to school able to recite the ordered names of the smaller whole numbers, typically one through ten, and sometimes one to twenty or beyond.

The written numerals greater than ten follow a strict pattern that reflects the numeration system we use. While the English spoken numerals generally follow the same pattern, there are some confusing exceptions. We use a new name for each of the numbers zero through nine. A subset of these names, transformed in some cases, forms the stem sounds for naming the decades twenty through ninety. Often, as in forty-five, the decade name—a single digit name followed by the sound *ty*—is easily identifiable. Sometimes, as in thirty-six, a small transformation has been made in the unit name. Unfortunately, the numbers eleven through nineteen do not follow a pattern closely at all. Ten, eleven, and twelve are named with completely new words, as if they were single digits like zero or nine. Furthermore, not only do the numbers thirteen through nineteen reverse the naming order of the rest of the decades but also *teen* has no apparent relationship to the number of collected tens, as is found with the names of the higher decades. (To make matters worse for the child learning to write 13, the sounds *thir* for the 3 and *teen* for the 1 must be written in reverse order. For a child, especially one who is learning to read by the phonics method or who has reversal difficulty, this exception does violence to a not-so-secure mental structure.) For much of counting, however, there is a pattern, and children who eventually understand this pattern are not faced with having to memorize 100 new, unrelated sounds to count to 100.

books

That many children can count to ten upon school entrance does not relieve the teacher of the task of making sure that *all* children can or will learn to count in the classroom. Luckily, this arithmetic skill comes with a built-in sugar coating. Few children do not enjoy being read to, and through the years a host of beautiful counting books have been written. Some of them are:

Becker, John. *Seven Little Rabbits*. New York: Scholastic Press, 1973.
Berenstein, Stanley, and Janice Berenstein. *Bears on Wheels*. New York: Random House, 1969.
Brown, Marc. *One, Two, Three: An Animal Counting Book*. Boston: Little, Brown and Company, 1976.

Emberley, Barbara. *One Wide River to Cross.* New York: Scholastic Press, 1966.

Feelings, Muriel. *Maja Means One: The Swahili Counting Book.* New York: Dial Press, 1976.

Hoban, Russell, and Sylvie Selig. *Ten What?: A Mystery Counting Book.* New York: Charles Scribner's Sons, 1979.

Hoban, Tana. *Count and See.* New York: Macmillan, 1972.

Keats, Ezra Jack. *Over in the Meadow.* New York: Scholastic Press, 1973.

Nolan, Dennis. *Monster Bubbles.* Englewood Cliffs, NJ: Prentice-Hall, 1976.

Sendak, Maurice. *One Was Johnny.* New York: Harper and Row, 1977.

Sesame Street Book of Numbers. New York: Signet Books, 1971.

Tudor, Tasha. *1 is One.* Skokie, Ill.: Rand McNally, 1956.

Wahl, John, and Stacey Wahl. *I Can Count the Petals of a Flower.* Reston, Va.: NCTM, 1976.

Wildsmith, Brian. *Brian Wildsmith's 1, 2, 3.* New York: Franklin Watts, 1965.

Young (1979) lists a great many more, and any children's librarian can bring you up to date on the newest additions to this genre.

fingerplays, verses, and songs

Some states list as a duty of the teacher the encouragement of physical activity and singing. Adding counting games and songs to the early school program is a superior example of hitting two targets at once. Among the many possible choices, here are a few you might want to share with young children. *Do* memorize them if you are going to use them. A teacher who directs songs with one eye on the prompt sheet is not nearly as effective as one who can give his or her whole attention to the children. Unfortunately, authors cannot be credited for most of these because they are part of the oral tradition.

Let's begin with an old favorite.

One, Two, Buckle My Shoe

One, two, buckle my shoe
Three, four, shut the door
Five, six, pick up sticks
Seven, eight, lay them straight
Nine, ten, a big fat hen

Eleven, twelve, dig and delve
Thirteen, fourteen, maids a'counting
Fifteen, sixteen, maids in the kitchen
Seventeen, eighteen, maids a'waiting
Nineteen, twenty, my plate's empty.

This verse can be made more instructive if each of twenty children is given a numeral to raise when the number word is called.

This more rolicking counting-backwards verse may be new to you. Use a singsong rhythm, and overplay each motion.

Ten Little Monkeys

Ten little monkeys, jumping on the bed
   (Your ten fingers are the monkeys. Your leg is the bed.
   Bounce your fingers up and down.)
One (hold up one finger) fell off and broke his head.
Called (hold imaginary phone to ear) for the doctor and
   the doctor said,
"No more monkeys, jumping on the bed!"
   (Wag index finger in a semicircle, making eye contact
   with various children as you do.)
Nine little monkeys . . . and so on, down to "one little monkey."

There is some surprise action in this next fingerplay, which will delight most children.

The Hive of Bees

Here is a beehive
   (Hold hand in a fist, back of hand up.)
Where are the bees?
Hidden inside where nobody sees.
Now they come creeping
Out of the hive.
   (Extend finger, one at a time as you count.)
One, two, three, four, five.
Bzzzzzzzzz.
   (Tickle person next to you.)

These two seasonal verses feature ordinal numbers as well as cardinal numbers.

Valentines

Five little valentines, pretty with lace
Standing in a row, in their own place.
The first one says, "Will you be mine?"
The second one says, "Be my Valentine!"
The third one says, "I love you."
The fourth one says, "I'll be true."
The fifth one says, "Let's all run away
And find a little friend today."

Jack-o-Lanterns

Five little jack-o-lanterns sitting on a gate
   (Place five children holding jack-o-lanterns in a row of chairs.)
The first one said, "My, it's getting late."
The second one said, "Who goes there?"
The third one said, "There are ghosts in the air."
The fourth one said, "Let's run, let's run."
The fifth one said, "Isn't Halloween fun?"
Puff went the wind and out went the light.
   (Turn out light.)
And off ran the jack-o-lanterns on Halloween night.
   (Children run off.)

These last two songs adapt well to acting out with hand puppets or as a brief skit with the children. Such presentations are much appreciated by parents for visiting day entertainments. They have the added advantage of requiring many children, none of whom has a great deal of responsibility.

Here are a pair of fingerplays about birds. Both are good circle-time activities.

One Little Brown Bird

One little brown bird, up and up she flew   (Raise one finger.)
Along came another, and that made two.   (Raise a second.)
Two little brown birds, sitting in a tree   (Raise a second.)
Along came another one, and that made three.   (Raise a third.)
Three little brown birds, here comes one more   (Raise a fourth)
What's all the noise about? That made four.   (Flutter the four fingers.)
Four little brown birds, and one makes five   (Raise the thumb.)
Singing in the sun, glad to be alive.

Five Little Chickadees

Five little chickadees, sitting on the floor
   (Hold up hand, fingers extended.)
One flew away and then there were four.
   (Fold down one finger as each bird flies away.)
Four little chickadees, sitting in a tree
One flew away and then there were three.
Three little chickadees, looking at you
One flew away and then there were two.
Two little chickadees sitting in the sun
One flew away and then there was one.
One little chickadee sitting alone
He flew away and then there was none.

From A. A. Milne, creator of Winnie-the-Pooh, the delightful "When I Was One." Have the children act it out by "growing" as you read the verse aloud.

When I Was One

When I was one	When I was five
I had just begun.	I was just alive.
When I was two	But now I'm six
I was nearly new.	I'm as clever as clever.
When I was three	So I think I'll be six
I was hardly me.	now for ever and ever.
When I was four	
I was not much more.	

Many, many songs use counting. Here is *my* all-time favorite counting song. It must be sung standing in a tight circle.

Alice the Camel

Alice the camel had five humps.
  (Swing one hand with all five
    fingers up, in time with the music.)
Alice the camel had five humps.
  (Continue.)
Alice the camel had five humps.
  (Continue.)
Go, Alice, go!
Boom, Boom, Boom.
  (Bump the hip of the person on
  each side of you on each word.)

Second Verse:
Alice the camel had four humps.
  (Put down one finger;
    swing hand as before.)

(REPEAT with three humps, two humps, one hump, and no humps.)

Then sing:
Alice the camel was a horse
  (Swing fist in air) (repeat two times
    more)
Go, Alice, go!
  (No bumps this time, but raise the fist
  in the air on each "Go!", as if
  cheering.)

"Alice" has a catchy beat, more like a dance beat than a nursery rhyme. The only trouble with "Alice" is that it is infectious. Teachers who have learned this song report they find themselves singing it at strange times, "booms" and all.

One of the most delightful of all counting songs is the lyrical "Over in the Meadow." At least two book versions of this song are available, one by Ezra Jack Keats and the other by John Lanstaff and Feodor Rojankovsky.

Over in the Meadow

Over in the meadow in the sand in the sun
Lived an old mother turtle and her little turtle one.
"Dig," said the mother. "We dig," said the one,
So they dug all day in the sand in the sun.

Over in the meadow where the stream runs blue
Lived an old mother fish and her little fishes two.
"Swim," said the mother. "We swim," said the two,
So they swam all day where the stream runs blue.

Over in the meadow in a hole in a tree
Lived old mother owl and her little owls three.
"Tu-whoo," said the mother. "Tu-whoo," said the three,
So they tu-whooed all day in a hole in a tree.

Over in the meadow by the old barn door
Lived an old mother rat and her little ratties four.
"Gnaw," said the mother. "We gnaw," said the four,
So they gnawed all day by the old barn door.

Over in the meadow in a snug bee hive
Lived an old mother bee and her little bees five.
"Buzz," said the mother. "We buzz," said the five,
So they buzzed all day in a snug bee hive.

Over in the meadow in a nest built of sticks
Lived an old mother crow and her little crows six.
"Caw," said the mother. "We caw," said the six.
So they cawed all day in a nest built of sticks.

Over in the meadow where the grass grows so even
Lived an old mother frog and her little froggies seven.
"Jump," said the mother. "We jump," said the seven,
So they jumped all day where the grass grows so even.

Over in the meadow by the old mossy gate
Lived an old mother lizard and her little lizards eight.
"Bask," said the mother. "We bask," said the eight,
So they basked all day by the old mossy gate.

Over in the meadow by the old scotch pine
Lived an old mother duck and her little ducks nine.
"Quack," said the mother. "We quack," said the nine,
So they quacked all day by the old scotch pine.

Over in the meadow in a cozy wee den
Lived an old mother beaver and her little beavers ten.
"Beave," said the mother. "We beave," said the ten,
So they beaved all day in a cozy wee den.

For simplicity it's hard to beat "The Button Song." It is fun to sing this song as you count the buttons on a child's coat or, with a slight word change, count the raisins in cookies or the swallows on a telephone line.

The Button Song
One button, two buttons, three buttons,
Four buttons (continue as needed)
And not a button more.

This next song was being sung by Captain Kangaroo many years ago when the author's children were young. It is still a favorite.

Ten in the Bed
There were ten in the bed,
And the little one said, "Roll over. Roll over."
So they all rolled over and one fell out.

(Repeat with nine, eight . . . two.)

Last verse:
There was one in the bed
And the little one said,
"Goodnight."

A song made popular by the motion picture *The Inn of the Sixth Happiness* was entitled "The Children's Marching Song." Most of us know it better as "This Old Man."

This Old Man
This old man, he say one (Raise one finger.)
He play knick-knack on my thumb (Touch thumb.)
With a knick-knack (Pound left thumb with right hand.)
Paddy-whack (Pound right thumb with left hand.)
Give the dog a bone (Toss imaginary bone over right shoulder.)
This old man (Pull "beard" with right hand.)
Comes rolling home. (Roll hands one over the other.)

The rhymes for the other verses are:

Two—shoe
Three—knee

Four—door ("pretend" a door)
Five—hive (ditto)
Six—sticks
Seven—up to heaven (shake hand in air)
Eight—pate (that's your head)
Nine—on his spine
Ten—all again

As you can see, "This Old Man" degenerates quickly after four. You may want to keep the song short.

Another old man is Noah—and what a fine song he inspired. If you don't know this one, please try to learn it. The tune is a nice change from the usual childhood melodies and can be found in *One Wide River to Cross* by Barbara Emberly (Scholastic Press, 1966).

One Wide River to Cross

Old Noah built himself an ark.
One more river to cross.
He made it out of hickory bark.
One more river to cross.
Chorus:
One more river and that wide river is Jordan.
One more river, there's one more river to cross.
(Don't get impatient, *now* we finally start counting!)
The animals came one by one.
One more river to cross.
The bear was chewing a cinnamon bun.
One more river to cross.
(Sing chorus.)
The animals came two by two—the aligator lost his shoe.
The animals came three by three—the fly, the gnat, and the bumblebee.
The animals came four by four—the hippo, she got stuck in the door.
The animals came five by five—the yak in slippers did arrive.
The animals came six by six—the elephants did funny tricks.
The animals came seven by seven—a drop of rain fell out of heaven.
The animals came eight by eight—some came in by roller skate.
The animals came nine by nine—the cats and kittens kept in line.
The animals came ten by ten—let's go back and sing it again.

Ready for an *active* song? Try "Johnny's Hammer." The first hammer is your right hand, held in a fist. The second hammer is your left hand. The third, your right foot; the fourth, your left foot. When it's time to work with five hammers, your head is called into action. To "work" is to move up and down. In the case of hammers 3 and 4 this involves pounding on the floor. (You teach in a first-floor classroom, I hope.)

Johnny's Hammer

Johnny works with one hammer, one hammer, one hammer.
Johnny works with one hammer, then he works with two.
(Repeat with two, three, four and five. Then sing in reverse order: five, four, three, two, one.)
Last verse:
Johnny works with one hammer, one hammer, one hammer.
Johnny works with one hammer, then he goes to sleep.
(The last line should be sung in decreasing tempo, and singers should rest their heads on their hands for the last word.)

Many people know the next one as a folk song. It is also a fine counting song.

I'll Sing You One-O!

I'll sing you one-o!
Green grow the rushes, O!
What is your one-o?
One is one and all alone and evermore shall be so.
I'll sing you two-o.
Green grow the rushes-o!
What is your two-o?
Two, two the little white boys
Clothes all in green, O.
One is one and all alone and evermore shall be so.
The rest of the verses follow a similar format:
Three—three, three, the rivals
Four—four for the gospelmakers
Five—five for the five bright shiners
Six—six for the six who never got fixed
Seven—seven for the pearly gates of heaven
Eight—eight for the eight that stood at the gate
Nine—nine for the nine dressed so fine
Ten—ten for the Ten Commandments
Eleven—eleven for the eleven that went to heaven
Twelve—twelve for the twelve apostles

Here's another happy little tune dealing with the outdoors. Some teachers may have learned it at summer camp when they were young themselves.

Five Little Speckled Frogs

Five little speckled frogs
Sat on a speckled log
Eating a most delicious bug. (yum! yum!)
One jumped into the pool
Where it was nice and cool
Now there are four speckled frogs. (glug! glug!)
Four little speckled frogs
Sat on a speckled log
Eating a most delicious bug. (yum! yum!)
One jumped into the pool
Where it was nice and cool
Now there are three speckled frogs. (glug! glug!)
(Repeat with three, two, and one.)

Yet another countdown song is the following. This is delightful when performed with a cast of three.

Three Blue Pigeons

Three Blue Pigeons
Sitting on a wall
Three blue pigeons
Sitting on a wall
One flew away. (oooh!)

Two blue pigeons
Sitting on a wall
Two blue pigeons
Sitting on a wall
The second flew away. (oooh!)

One blue pigeon
Sitting on a wall
One blue pigeon
Sitting on a wall
The third flew away. (oooh!)

No blue pigeons
Sitting on a wall

No blue pigeons
Sitting on a wall
One flew back. (yeah!)

One blue pigeon
Sitting on a wall.
One blue pigeon
Sitting on a wall
A second flew back. (yeah!)

Two blue pigeons
Sitting on a wall
Two blue pigeons
Sitting on a wall
A third flew back. (yeah!)

Three blue pigeons
Sitting on a wall
Three blue pigeons
Sitting on a wall!

A long but popular counting song is "Twelve Days of Christmas." In case you've forgotten, here is what "my true love gave to me" on the twelfth day:

Twelve drummers drumming
Eleven pipers piping
Ten lords a' leaping
Nine ladies dancing
Eight maids a' milking
Seven swans a' swimming
Six geese a' laying
Five gold rings
Four calling birds
Three French hens
Two turtle doves
And a partridge in a pear tree.

Accompanying the children adds dimension to the experience of singing in the classroom, and you don't have to play the piano to do it. You can accompany the children on a guitar or on a recorder just as well. The best choise of all may be just to sing along with them. When people sing together, a special closeness results. I hope you will let this magic be felt in your classroom.

nine

writing the numerals

Child Margaret

The child Margaret begins to write numbers on a Saturday
morning, the first numbers formed under her wishing
child fingers.

All the numbers come well-born, shaped in figures assertive for a frieze in a child's room.

Both 1 and 7 are straightforward, military, filled with
lunge and attack, erect in shoulder-straps.

The 6 and 9 salute as dancing sisters, elder and younger,
and 2 is a trapeze actor swinging to handclaps.

The numbers are well-born, only 3 has a hump on its
back and the 8 is knock-kneed.

The child Margaret kisses all once and gives two kisses to
3 and 8.

(Each number is a brand-new rag doll. . . . 0 in the wishing
fingers . . . millions of rag dolls!!)

Carl Sandburg

In the process of becoming educated, children must learn to write the
symbols for numbers used in our culture. Although many children by the
age of five or six may be able to count by rote and to count objects in a small
group, fewer learn to read or write the numerals before coming to school.

As adults, we are so comfortable doing both these things that we sometimes underestimate the difficulty faced by a small child who must learn to copy, recognize, and name thirty-six scribbles, some of which are combined into words and some of which tell "how many" or "how much."

From the onset, one thing must be crystal clear—the ability to write numerals is not at all the same as the ability to understand their value or to process them correctly. Certainly the numerals must be legible. Mathematical computations, after all, are a means of keeping a record and/or communicating with another person. But inability to write a numeral should not be confused with inability to succeed at mathematics. Likewise, making beautiful numerals is not the same as being able to think about number or to use numbers to solve real-world problems. After all, people like Leonardo da Vinci and Einstein were noted for their *poor* handwriting as well as for their extraordinary mathematical and scientific achievements.

the fading technique

The ability to write numerals is a skill—and from your own experience you know some of us have acquired it better than others. One of the best ways to teach this skill is to use a sequence of steps based on the work of Skinner called *fading.* In this technique a vivid model is gradually "faded out" until the learner functions without any clues at all. Many of us used this technique when we were asked to memorize a list of dates in history. At first we read the material from the book several times. When we felt we were able, we glanced at fewer and fewer of the dates. Finally, we recited the whole list on our own with maybe just a whispered syllable or two of help from a friend. This sequence of presentation of clues from complete to partial and finally to nonexistent is the proper framework for planning lessons on forming numerals or letters. A word about when such instruction is appropriate: Writing numerals is not very different from learning to write letters and should be part of the ordinary penmanship practice in your classroom. It need not be part of the mathematical lesson, though such lessons provide opportunities for practice. Any bad grades that must be given for imprecision in conforming to cultural expectations should be penmanship grades and not mathematics grades.

penmanship prerequisites

All successful attempts at writing—numerals included—require the attainment of prewriting skills. Among these are the ability to grasp the writing instrument, position the paper, and copy from a model. Some children, although they are "on level" in many other respects, may take longer to acquire these prerequisite skills and to develop the proficiency at writing numerals. This may be true of some children who are good at gross motor skills such as running and jumping as well as of those who are chronically neurologically impaired. Some learning-disabled children may have such difficulty holding a pencil that writing is nearly rendered impossible. For these children Johnson and Micklebust (1971) suggest the use of large hexagonal crayons or pencils, which afford a solid grip. Be sure to replace them before they are too short. Fixing a small piece of tape on the tool where it should rest on the index finger will help the child develop a proper hold. Commercial guides for round pencils which accomplish this same goal are also available.

People are not born knowing how to slant their writing paper. They must be taught. According to tradition, for manuscript writing the edge of the paper should be parallel with the edge of the table and for cursive writing the paper should tilt about sixty degrees to the left for right-handers and about sixty degrees to the right for most left-handers (Johnson and Miklebust 1971). Recent research has raised questions concerning the wisdom of deciding for others how they should place the paper, however. Some left-handers achieve better results using the position customary for right-handers and, more rarely, vice versa. These variations appear to arise from differences in the organization of the functions within the brain (Davidson 1979). Although it used to be the norm to attempt to "change" left-handers, it now seems wise to allow each child to use whichever hand seems natural and to tilt the paper as is comfortable for that child.

Before they are asked to copy numerals and letters, children should be able to copy confidently from simpler models such as 〉 and /\/\ When this "real" schoolwork begins, undiagnosed vision problems may become apparent. Should this happen in your room, be sure to refer students for further diagnosis.

Apart from merely seeing the material to be copied, the child must have good near and far vision. In addition, he or she must have good hand

and eye coordination and sufficient short-term memory to copy material without losing place. All these skills need to be developed. Activities that will foster these skills may seem far removed from writing practice, but this is a case in which the direct route is not the best route. Finger painting, pouring water, stringing beads, hanging clothes on a line, connecting dots, molding clay, catching balls of various sizes, bowling with large balls and pins, filling bottles with sand or rice, and playing finger games—these familiar kindergarten activities have an educational *raison d'etre* when it comes to writing readiness.

When a child begins to write a numeral, say 3, it is helpful if an adult describes each part of the numeral. The sequential "first we do this, and then we do this" approach provides structure. Leaving the completed figure on the board and drawing a second model while the children watch is also helpful. Before attempting to write on paper, children can profit from following a moving flashlight with hand and eye as it makes a figure and tracing in the air with either the index finger alone or the middle and the index fingers held together. For some of us, visualizing comes more easily if our eyes are closed. Some children are helped if they say the numeral's name as they draw it (Wittrock 1978). Employing all these strategies will increase the probability of efficient, painless learning.

reversals

It would be an atypical classroom that did not include several children who sometimes, or frequently, reversed numerals. Left-right orientation is not a relevant feature for young children. Some children, especially left-handers, reverse letters and numerals on a consistent basis well into second grade. Others do so only occasionally. Many do so when under stress, as on a test or timed piece of work. Some children reverse all the numerals; some have trouble only with 3, 5, and 9. Some children consistently reverse particular numerals or may be mirror writers, reversing not only each letter, both in form and in order within the word, but also the words themselves. Parents of these children are apt to be shocked and distressed when they first see those "backwards" papers (Figure 9–1). They will be forever grateful to the teacher who tells them, as my son's teacher did me, that many entirely normal but immature writers exhibit this behavior. Consistent modeling of the correct forms, and corrected

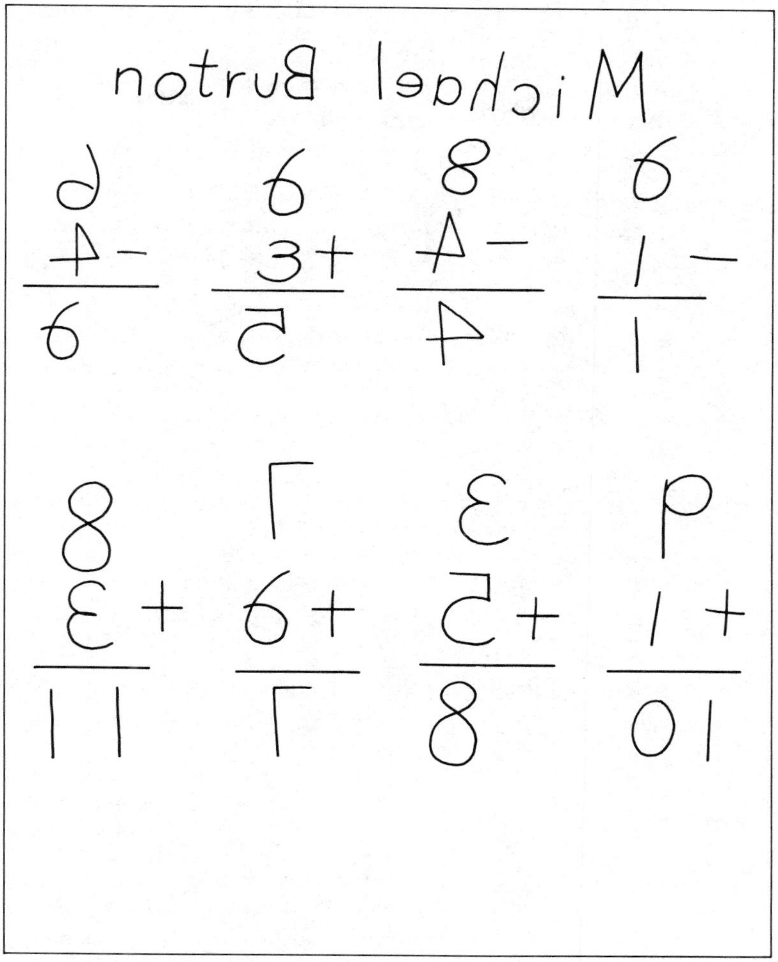

Figure 9–1   A Mathematics Paper Written in Mirror Image

practice and praise for continued effort will by the middle of the second grade, solve the problem for all but a few children who may need more intensive help. A specialist in learning disabilities can provide assistance at this point, but is seldom needed before then.

Reversals are so common because the form of the symbols is arbitrary. Nothing inherently in 3 makes it apparent that it should face the way it does; therefore, each numeral's form must be memorized. This task is more difficult than many of us imagine because, until the age of seven or eight, the concepts of left and right are not firmly established (Piaget 1950). What the child is asked to do, then, is learn to execute upon command arbitrary arrangements of lines and curves and, moreover, learn the names of these and twenty-six other symbols at the same time. You might be able to get a feeling for the task if you ask a friend to make some scribbles for you and you try to copy them while you look not at your paper but in a mirror. Of course, the child is also adjusting to a new way of life, more children than he or she had probably ever seen at close range before, new time schedules and routines, and a whole group of strange adults giving suggestions and/or orders. College freshmen often report feeling disoriented and confused, this is but a pale reflection of what the first-time-to-school child experiences.

dominance tests

Some children are especially hampered in their attempts to learn to read and write. Most of us are right-eyed, right-armed, and right-footed, and right-handed or left-handed, left-armed, left-eyed, and left-footed. Mixed dominance children have a blend of these. You may be interested in trying a few simple tests to get an indication of your own dominance pattern.

1. Hand dominance:
   a. Pretend you are lifting a fork. Which hand did you use? That is probably your dominant hand.
   b. Fold your hands in your lap. The thumb on top is probably on your nondominant hand.
2. Arm dominance:
   a. Cross your arms on your chest. Your dominant arm is most likely closer to your body.
3. Leg dominance:
   a. Stand up and take three steps. In most cases, the dominant foot is kept on the ground longer.
   b. Try to balance on each foot in turn. Which one was easier? That one is probably your dominant foot.
4. Eye dominance:
   a. Roll up a tube of paper and place an X on the wall or desk. Look through the tube with both eyes and locate the X. Close each eye in turn without moving the tube. When you see the X again, you will probably have your dominant eye open.

Some children of mixed dominance have a more difficult time with schoolwork than similarly able children with similar experiences; others do not. Rather than guessing ahead of time who will take longer to reach a desired level of proficiency, just be ready to offer help to any youngster who needs it.

Occasionally a child will write with either hand equally well. When either hand is equally comfortable, encouraging these "ambidextrous" children to use their right hand may prove the kindest course. Societal sensitivity toward providing for "lefties" is still in its infancy.

instructional techniques

When you begin teaching the writing of numerals, please remember that close supervision is important. It is easier to correct faulty habits before they have become well established. A real help to the left-handed children in the class of a right-handed teacher is the teacher's learning to write left-handed on the board so that the numeral can be directly modeled. The converse case also applies, of course. Not all teachers will be able to manage this, but it is a kindness to young learners to try.

Having a model of the numerals on each child's desk as well as on the board will aid children who have trouble copying from a distance or copying from a vertical to a horizontal surface. Encouraging children to cross out rather than erase unsatisfactory attempts will save many smudgy, torn papers and will provide the teacher with valuable diagnostic data (Thurber 1978).

The forms of the numerals we use have no significance. Several hypotheses, however, have been advanced to explain the shapes they have taken (Cajori 1928). Despite this lack of basis for the acceptable forms, models of the numerals should be consistently drawn. A sample of currently accepted forms is given in Figure 9–2, page 76. Because 4 often looks different when it is written from when it appears in type, you will want to be sure the children realize 4 and 4 represent the same quantity. People who have adopted one form of making a 5 may find it difficult to accept the other form. Both, however are widely used and neither is an aberant case; so flexibility is called for.

In learning to write the numerals, children need not begin with making pencil marks on paper. A first step to writing is often tracing a model. When models are purchased or made, be sure all the digits (0, 1, 2, 3, 4, 5, 6, 7, 8, and 9) are included. Some models that can be traced by children are the following.

1.   A set of sandpaper numerals. If you can afford several sets made from various grades of paper, you will have a fine fading device.
2.   A set of yarn cards. On cards designed to be used at the beginning of the teaching sequence, glue heavy package-tying yarn to posterboard. For cards to be used later, use finer yarn.
3.   Fabric numerals. Cut the numerals from heavy tweed or corduroy and glue them onto cards.
4.   Wooden, Styrofoam, or sponge models. Both the "hole" made by the numeral and the cut-out numeral itself can be traced.

Once the child can trace the numerals with ease, a variety of activities can give an opportunity for practice with or without a model. Providing a variety often will provide an incentive for practice.

1.   Writing the numerals on another person's back. The "drawee" gets to guess the numeral drawn.
2.   Painting numerals on the chalkboard or sidewalk with a big brush and a can of water.
3.   Drawing numerals on newsprint, adding machine paper, or computer paper with large felt-tip markers.
4.   Bending pipe cleaners or just-cooked spaghetti.
5.   Drawing the numerals in sand, cornmeal, or salt that has been poured into a pan or on a paper plate smeared with finger paint or pudding.
6.   Writing the numerals in the air with a nose or an elbow as well as a finger.
7.   Molding Playdough or cookie dough numerals.
8.   Stretching elastic bands to form numerals on a geoboard.

Figure 9–2   *Forms of the Numerals*

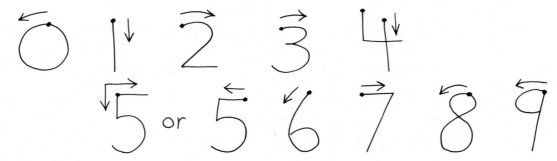

9.   Making the numerals on the back of the hand with roll-on cologne or a moistened cotton swab.

10.   Gluing beans, corn, or seeds onto a card in the shape of a numeral named by the teacher.

11.   Walking, hopping, or skipping around a numeral made with masking tape on the floor.

12.   Writing the numeral with a stylus on a "magic" slate. These waxed boards, available at variety and discount stores, allow mistakes to disappear when the plastic film is lifted. They allow the child to make several attempts but only a final, acceptable product needs to be shown to the teacher.

Children are usually eager to practice the grown-up activity of writing the numerals on paper. Some sample practice worksheets are given in Figure 9–3. The colors indicate first (green) and second (red) strokes in the second figure. Position guides are also used. Care should be taken to

Figure 9–3   Sample Writing Practice Cards

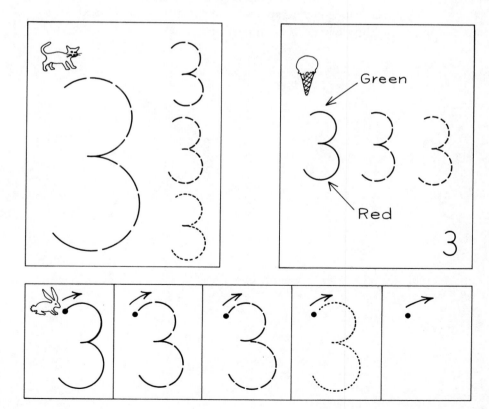

distinguish top from bottom in any material presented to children. You and your class might plan together some other ways, this can be shown. Smiley faces, ice-cream-cone clues, or simple line drawings as are used here are some possibilities.

It is easy to underestimate the task of writing numerals because adults perform it so effortlessly. But

> learning to write is not a mechanical, lower-level reflex response, but a thinking process, entailing activity of the cortical nerve areas. Smooth motor coordination of eye and hand, control of arm, hand, and finger muscles are acquired in the process of learning to write and are needed for legible results. Learning to write also requires maturity adequate for accurate perception of the symbol patterns. Writing from memory demands the retention of visual and kinesthetic images of forms, not present to the senses, for future recall (Hildreth 1947, 583–584).

Writing the numerals with ease will pay dividends when computation is to be done. When numeral writing becomes second nature, the mind is freed to concentrate on other matters. The next step is also crucial: reading what has been written.

ten

recognizing the numerals

Most reading and writing exercises in beginning number work should consist of supervised corrected practice. Part of this practice often includes the presentation of a numeral and the request for its name. While being shown a standard numeral form and being asked to make another just like it, the child is often told the name of the figure and asked to repeat it while drawing. Having a label for the figure helps imprint it in the memory. The ability to match numerals precedes the ability to recognize and name them, and the latter skill is prerequisite to the ability to correctly associate the written symbol with a set of a given size (Wang, Resnick, and Boozer 1971). Because most children have some ability to count objects, the practice exercises often include showing a picture of from one to three objects and asking that the child write how many or circle the number that tells how many objects are in the picture.

making it meaningful

In general, the form of the numeral is no clue to its referent number, although Stern has used a technique to tie the numeral and number together (Figure 10–1, page 80) and similar procedures have been hypothesized in the past, as Cajori (1928) has documented. One system supposedly determined the shape of the figure and number of angles

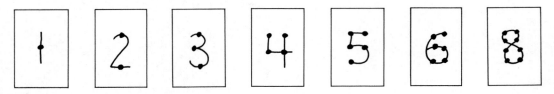

Figure 10–1   *Stern's Dotted Numerals*

formed, but you can see the system was especially weak in explaining the 4, 7, and 9 and is not in general use.

It is somewhat difficult to separate recognition of the numerals from development of the concept of numbers, but it can be done, of course. Recognition can mean rote name calling upon the presentation of a symbol stimulus. If this is all that is desired, spaced practice, contingent reward schedules, and ample opportunity to display the behavior are all that are needed, but such a regimen is not recommended. As much as possible, doing mathematics should be a meaningful activity; therefore, much of the material introduced in this section will be further elaborated on in the later section on developing the concept of number.

One of the most effective devices for teaching numeral recognition to children who can count is the numeral card (Figure 10–2), which consists of three cards attached to two metal rings. The top two cards are shorter than the bottom card. On the top card is the first stroke used in writing the numeral, written in green. On the second card is the completed numeral, written in green and red. On the third card is the numeral written in black, the number word in print, and a model set illustrating "how many."

Figure 10–2   *Numeral Cards (Adapted from Baratta-Lorton 1976, 363)*

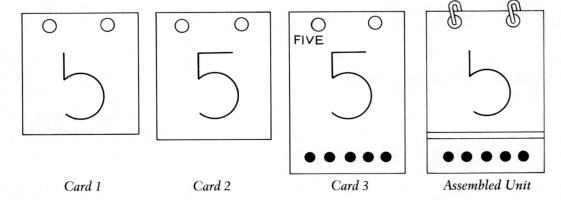

Card 1   Card 2   Card 3   Assembled Unit

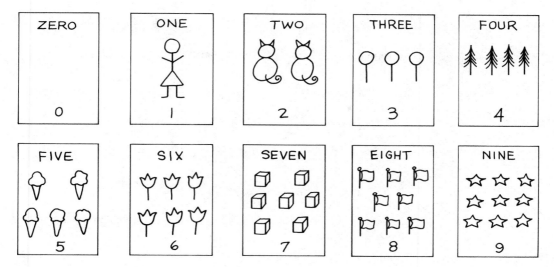

Figure 10–3   Set of Model Sets

Model sets have long been popular instructional aids. They may merely display items, (Figure 10–3), or they may be cards or paper plates with the numerals and number names written on them; the child places on each the number of objects required (Figure 10–4). They might also be puzzles (Figure 10–5, page 81). Sometimes strip cards are used (Figure 10–6). Here the child pulls the top strip through until a set shows in the window and then pulls the bottom strip through until the correct numeral shows. For beginners, the sets and appropriate numeral are often color coded. This feature, helpful at first, is not conducive to true learning and

Figure 10–4   Cards for Objects

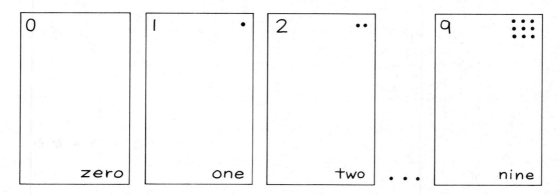

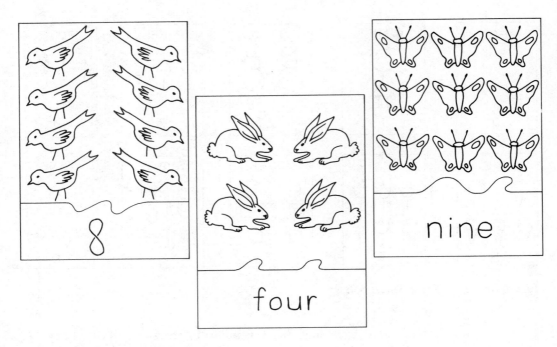

Figure 10–5   *Jigsaw Puzzles*

should be omitted after the introductory lessons. The numerals and sets should be in random order, and some type of self-checking device should be incorporated by the teacher. A somewhat more structured aid is the

Figure 10–6   *Strip Card*

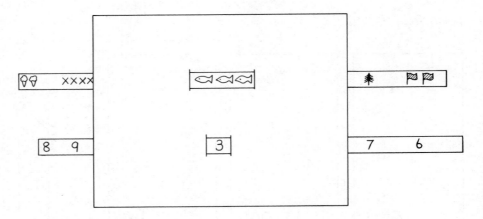

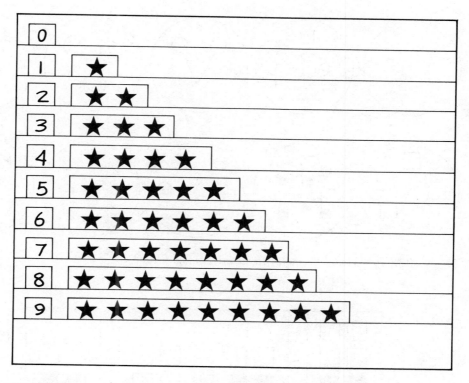

Figure 10–7   *Pocket Chart with Numeral Cards and Strips*

numeral strip chart (Figure 10–7). Here the set is composed of the same element, and the strip length is proportional to the numeral being matched.

It is worth mentioning that there has been long-standing disagreement on whether items in the model sets should be presented in random order to encourage counting (Figure 10–8, page 83), in patterns that vividly emphasize the "one more time" concept (Figure 10–9), or in the familiar domino patterns (Figure 10–10, page 84) or card patterns (Figure 10–11). The author knows of no research that has answered this question in a definitive way.

Some mathematics educators have been concerned that the increase in value should be modeled by a proportionate increase, as in Figure 10–7. Stern (1949) was one of the first to develop a full arithmetic program using this idea. Her counting board (Figure 10–12, page 86) combines counting and measurement. A child can either count the marked areas or can rely on the length of the rod. In the Cuisenaire material, the absence of unit

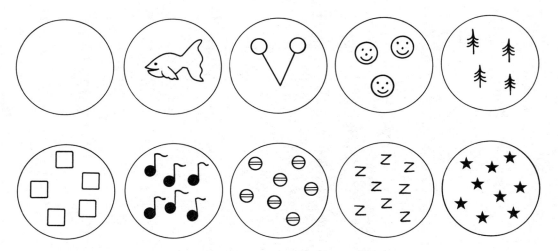

Figure 10–8   *Model Sets with Items in Random Order*

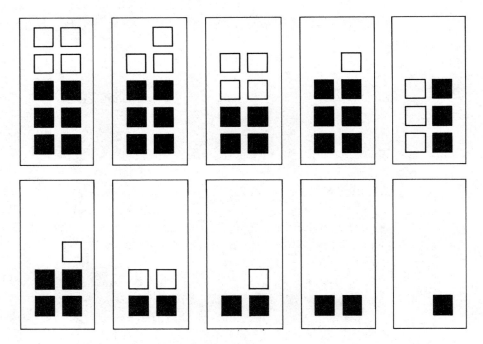

Figure 10–9   *Stern Number Pattern Boards*

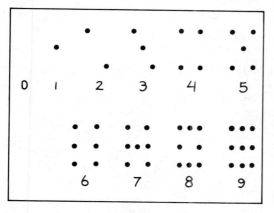

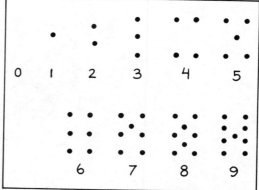

Figure 10–10   A Number Chart Using
                Domino Patterns

Figure 10–11   A Number Chart Using
                Playing Card Patterns

marks renders the counting procedure impossible; it is a pure measurement approach. Piaget (1952) believes such an approach may hinder rather
than assist a child's development of a concept of number, because each rod,
regardless of its length, can be considered "one."

Learning the sequence of the numerals is often tied to the use of a
number line. The number track shown in Figure 10–13 (page 86) is a
particularly well-developed number line. When the number bars shown in
Figure 10–12 are laid between the sides of the track, the end of the bar is
flush with the numeral displayed on the top of the counting board. The
numeral sequence can also be learned by using a template such as is shown
in Figure 10–14 (page 87). Here the child can trace the numerals in
sequence between evenly-spaced models.

Finally, the teacher can adapt a hundred board for use in teaching the
sequence of numerals. A handmade device, a hundred board begins with a
square yard of plywood and 100 nails or cup hooks. To make such a board,
first stain or paint the wood. Then put a handle on the top edge so you can
easily cart it around. Either a drawer handle or a twist of electrical wire
will prove suitable. Next, rule off on the board ten equally spaced rows and
columns, and place a nail or cup hook at each intersection. On each of the
100 nails or cup hooks, hang a metal-bound paper key tab (or a circle cut
from an index card and punched with a paper punch). The board is now
ready for use.

With young children, the teacher might have the group count in
unison as he or she hangs the disks up one by one. Either disks with the

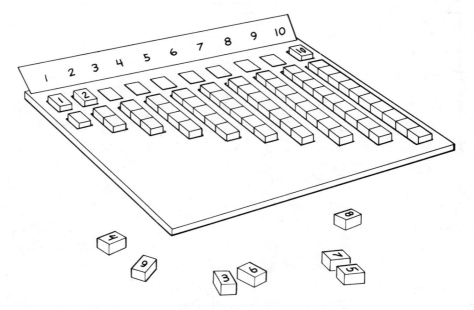

Figure 10–12   *Stern Counting Board*

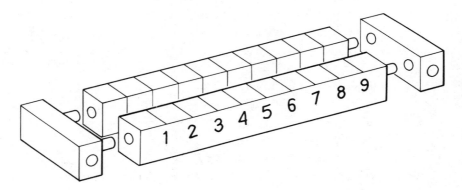

Figure 10–13   *Stern Number Track with Bumpers*

numbers written on them or blank disks may be used. When sequence is the focus of the lesson, the teacher can ask the students to turn the disks over one at a time and repeat the numeral name as its form is revealed. Figure 10–15 shows the board after the task of counting to five has been correctly executed. Later the children can be asked to count the disks in the top row, touching each one. Turning the last disk touched, they can ascertain if they counted correctly.

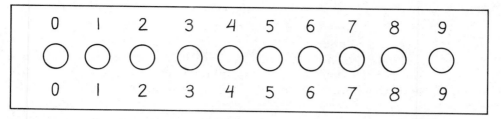

Figure 10–14   *A Number Line Template (Adapted from Baratta-Lorton 1976, 363)*

Numeral recognition can of course be strengthened if the numerals are displayed when counting rhymes are recited, if frequent attention is drawn to the many numerals that appear during the school day, and if games are used. Here are a few reinforcement activities.

Johnny, May I Cross Your River?

Divide the class into two lines facing each other across a space. Give each child a piece of paper with a number on it. One child (Johnny) stands in the middle and the other children say, "Johnny, may we cross your river?" Johnny says, "Only if you have number 4." All children with that number run to the opposite side, and Johnny tries to tag one person. The person tagged now takes Johnny's place in the middle, and the procedure is repeated.

Figure 10–15   *Hundred Board with Counter Disks*

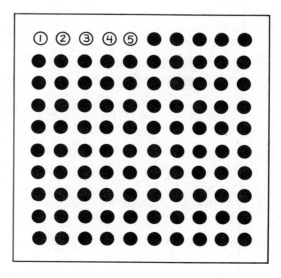

Number Train

Place one number card (0–9) on each of ten strings. Give
each of ten children a card to put around his or her neck,
and have the children make a train by holding the person
in front of them. Shuffling around the room to a song
like "Down by the Station" makes the learning more fun.

Recognition Bingo

Children love "Bingo," and it is an adaptable game. For number
recognition, have children place one numeral in each
of nine spaces on a small card. If the cards are covered
with contact paper first, the numerals can be changed for
each session. Numerals may be used more than once.
Hold up a picture of a group of items. If the child has
the numeral that tells how many are in that set, he or she
can cover the numeral. If the numeral appears more than
once, only one may be covered each time it is called.

Pendulum Swings

Choose a number. Write it on the board. Swing a weighted
piece of string or a necklace with a pendant that many times.
Have children count aloud as it swings back and forth. (Counting
as a clock strikes the hour is a related activity.)

a word on behalf of zero

The number zero holds a special place in elementary school mathematics, or at least it should. In times past and occasionally in times
present, zero is taught as a necessary evil—necessary because we must
have it to hold a place in our place value system. Zero was the latest
numeral added to our numeration system. Even its name was still in doubt
as late as the sixteenth century. Teachers sometimes say, "zero is not a
number, because if you don't have anything to count, you don't need a
number to count it." This approach can be very misleading. Of course 0
holds a place in 4065, because there are no hundreds left after the groups
of 1000 are made, but 6 is a place holder also; the use of the digits is exactly
analagous. The 6 tells how many groups of 10 there are; 0 tells how many
groups of 100 there are. To tell "how many" is a primary function of all
whole numbers, and zero does this as well as any other number does.

Some of us heard as children that zero is not really a number. It is time to put an end to this belief. It is important for children to learn from the start that the number telling how many live elephants are in the room is zero and that zero be included when numerals are written, sets made, or numbers discussed. Including zero as a natural part of the child's math activities will prevent the attachment of later-to-be-unlearned concepts to this number.

an awareness exercise

You may be wondering by now why so much time is being spent on such a simple task as learning to write and recognize numerals. The reason is that it isn't really a simple task at all. To prove this to yourself, look at the following list of number symbols and names. Practice writing the symbols a time or two with your nondominant hand.

Zip ∠

.	a ∖	. . . .	d ⊙	. . . . . .	g C	
. .	b ⊃	. . . .	e ∕	. . . .	h N	
. . .	c ∼	. . . . .	f ⟩	. . . .	i ╱	

Now test yourself. Cover the part of the page with the symbols and their explanations, and write the symbol for h, b, i, a, and zip. Not easy, is it?

Then imagine learning to compute: What is d + e ? f − b ? Write down the equation and the answer. Or consider place value—assume, for simplicity, you are in the base-10 system so familiar to you. Write the symbols for j, k, l, m, n, and o. Remember you have an advantage over young children because you not only have well-developed fine motor control and a good memory but also you know what "13" means.

Certainly this has been only a brief exposure to a new system and may seem an unfair test, but recall that you have a wealth of experience that is not part of the equipment a five-year-old brings to the study of mathematics. Trying to walk in the moccasins of such a child should help you become more tolerant of "silly errors" or "dumb mistakes." In mathematics, as in other parts of life, sometimes things seem easy only to those who have the skill; once you have a skill, it is difficult to imagine why anyone should need to struggle to attain it.

Working with numerals and numbers is rather like figure skating. When you watch professionals or gifted amateurs in competition, the jumps and turns look effortless. The hours of practice, and the multitude of mistakes are not evident. Their coaches, over a long time span, were patient yet held to high standards, gave encouragement yet offered suggestions for improvement. They would make a good model for the teacher who is helping children become comfortable with the world of numbers.

eleven

developing the concept of number

The culminating task of a child's first year of mathematics instruction is the development of a concept of number and the ability to communicate about number in oral and written form. Many of us came to our understanding of number by some fortuitous set of circumstances. Other children, less lucky, have gone through life seeing mathematics as the hopeless jumble described in poetry by Carl Sandberg.

Arithmetic

Arithmetic is where numbers fly like pigeons in and out of
 your head.
Arithmetic tells you how many you lose or win if you know
 how many you had before you lost or won.
Arithmetic is seven eleven all good children go to heaven—
 or five six bundle of sticks.
Arithmetic is numbers you squeeze from your head to your
 hand to your pencil to your paper till you get the answer.
Arithmetic is where the answer is right and everything is
 nice and you can look out of the window and see the blue
 sky—or the answer is wrong and you have to start all
 over and try again and see how it comes out this time. . . .

Piaget and others make a distinction between physical and logico-mathematical knowledge. The former requires only observation and abstraction on the lowest scale and gives a child the information to make such statements as "This is blue" or "There are lots of these." The latter requires reflection, and abstraction results in the creation of mental relationships. A child who has logico-mathematical knowledge can correctly make such statements as "There are as many blue ones as red ones" or "There are more here than there." An understanding of numbers is created by reflective abstraction by each child in the child's own mind. Unlike facts, number concepts cannot be transmitted through teacher talk. They must be abstracted by the young learners from repeated actions on material objects. The bases for number concepts are ordering and class inclusion (Kamii and De Vries 1976), and all the time the teacher has spent on these tasks will bear fruit when children attempt to understand, in a numerical sense, the world around them.

Exactly how children go about building up a concept of number is yet undetermined. Some mathematicians such as Poincaré believe number is constructed independently of logical structure and results from an intuitive understanding of $n + 1$. Others, such as Whitehead and Russell, reduce cardinal number to a concept of class and ordinal number to a concept of a transitive asymmetric relation. Piaget (1967) refutes both positions. "The whole number," he says, "is neither a simple system of class inclusions, nor a simple seriation, but an indissociable synthesis of inclusion and seriation. The synthesis derives from the abstraction of qualities and from the fact that these two systems (classification and seriation), which are distinct when their qualities are conserved, become fused as soon as their qualities are abstracted" (p. 83). It is the fusion that is paramount in the process. The cardinal and ordinal aspects of number, although often treated separately for convenience, are permanently bound together in a properly developed mental structure.

the conservation of number

Knowing the names of numbers merely provides labels for a child's interaction with quantity. No understanding of "twoness" or "fiveness" should be inferred from a child's ability to sing a number song. When and how do children acquire an understanding of number? Most of the questions generated in this area were initiated by Piaget's work concerning the child's ability to "conserve" numbers in the face of distracting clues.

Piaget's famous experiment for conservation consists of transforming one of two rows of candies. Each row contains four candies neatly lined up.

The adult, pointing to each row in turn, asks the child, "Are there more here or here or are there the same in each row?" Then the adult spreads

out one row of candies and repeats the question. A "conserver" is not fooled by the change in physical arrangements; a nonconserver is. A variation calls for two rows of candies, with five in one row and three in the other. A child is asked to count the candies in each row and tell if either row has more after changes are made in one row. For example, at first the rows look like this:

Then the same candies in one of the rows is moved to make the length of the rows more even:

Often children will respond correctly to the first situation and yet claim later when the same candies are rearranged that there is now an equal number of candies in each row. The distracting clues can be made even more pronounced, as in this arrangement

the child may even claim that the longer row with three candies has more. To prevent any misinterpretation of what is being asked, the interviewer often words the question something like, "If those were yours and these were mine, who would have the most to eat?" A change in language does not change the nonconserver's answer.

That the child doesn't really have a concept of number does not mean the child should not participate in mathematics lessons. We simply don't know enough about how conservation and early learning interact. The teacher must realize, however, that children can seem to possess a higher degree of understanding than they actualy do. A major significance of Piagetian research is its demonstration that children and adults understand things differently. Such a realization helps explain the persistent difficulty experienced by children especially in, say, linear measurement or in number sentences like $2 + \square = 5$. Tables 11–1, 11–2, and 11–3 (pages 106–108) list approximate age ranges from the attainment of the concepts of number and measurement as determined by Coxford (1963).

From much counting experience, most children acquire an understanding of the small numbers that approximates that of adults; that is, both children and adults mean the same thing when they say that the "fiveness" in five tells how many fingers are on one's right hand. Teachers and other adults who try to help children understand basic number concepts must offer example after example until the children discover the common feature of all sets containing five elements. Hence the very activities that provide for practice in counting also provide examples to help children discover the meaning of "twoness," "threeness," and so on.

An informal test of counting ability often used by kindergarten teachers is to ask a child how many dots are on a card containing two, three, or four dots and then to note the manner in which the child determines the answer. A child who "knows" how many objects make four is most apt to glance at the arrangement and quickly respond that there are four; one who has not yet learned "fourness" is more apt to carefully count each object before responding. Because some children will guess and others will think they must always count even when they know the answer, the test is not foolproof; still it offers the teacher a quick first estimate of the child's level of achievement.

helping children develop concepts

Helping children develop concepts is one of the most demanding tasks a teacher undertakes. It can be a most frustrating one, too. Because adults know so well what *five* means, it is difficult to remember that we didn't always know it. It seems so obvious an understanding that we sometimes become impatient when children seem to take a long time learning this concept. One of the best preparations a teacher can have is to experience difficulty in learning something. Perhaps if you contemplate a time when you were in a class in which the teacher seemed to believe something was very clear but you didn't "see" it at all, you will find it easier to have patience with young students. The frustration of "not getting it" and the joy when the light goes on are powerful emotions—children feel them, too.

When it comes to concepts, two very different instructional plans are suggested. Gagné (1977) believes mathematical learnings can be put into a hierarchy. The simplest steps of this ordered arrangement are associations (stimulus-response connections) and chains (verbal or motor sequences such as rote counting or making a numeral). The next higher type of learning is discriminations (identifying differences), and then come two types of concepts (signs of an ability to form classes). Concrete concepts depend also solely on sense-apparent data; defined concepts require definitions or the abstraction of a quality that is not sense apparent from a presented stimulus. *Red* is an example of a concrete concept; *five* is an example of a defined concept. [Gagné continues his hierarchy with rules (the relationship of two or more concepts) and higher-order rules (the use of rules to solve problems).] Gagné asserts that each learning type is based on the previous learning types and that school tasks can be ordered and should be taught with this in mind.

A more cognitively oriented approach, exemplified by Bruner (1960), suggests that concepts are best learned through guided discovery. He would offer a variety of suggestions including a structured questioning sequence, modeling by the teacher, providing interesting clues for the learner, and searching for patterns. The cognitive approach to concept learning is the one offered in this book, though Gagné's has much to offer as well.

Concepts require a learner to recognize similarities despite differences, a harder task than recognizing differences despite similarities. This recognition may be especially hard for some learning-disabled children and for those who have perceptual difficulties. Concept formation requires more than just being able to see or hear, but these certainly help.

There are several kinds of concepts (conjunctive, disjunctive, and relational), but all of them are taught in approximately the same way. (1) No matter what the concept, it is crucial that both examples and nonexamples be presented. If a child has only positive examples, there is nothing to test hypotheses against. (2) Concept formation is seldom rapid. Students need time to think about the material presented. (3) Discussion among students helps. (4) If the teacher can provide connections between what the students know already and what they are to learn, concept formation is both more rapid and more solid. (5) When materials are presented, visual or auditory clues (color coding, accenting important words) can be given to help students notice similarities and differences. (6)

Everything but the concept to be learned should be varied. In teaching the meaning of *five* for example, use a variety of materials, arrange them in many ways, and engage as many senses of the student as possible—all that should be constant is the number of objects. (7) Giving a student a label, *five* for example, helps the student store the information and retrieve it for later use. (8) When you want to see if the student has learned the concept, use a new material and/or configuration for the test—one never used as a class example. This avoids confusing what the student has memorized with what she or he understands.

All this is hard work for the teacher. Why bother? Because when a student sees the meaningfulness and interrelations between bits of mathematics, he or she can use them in new situations, remember them better, regenerate forgotten material, and apply what is known to problem-solving situations. Helping children learn concepts is, in the long run, an efficient way to proceed.

the counting task

Because children come to school with different home experiences, teachers can expect children who have achieved many different levels of counting skill. This makes program planning difficult. A typical class, for example, may contain a few children who can accurately count past 100, a few who can count past 20 but err someplace in the higher decades, a few who can count a little past 10, and a few who cannot count to 5.

Many children can count a single set. A more difficult task is to compare two sets of objects, which builds readiness of determining the equality and inequality of sets. For example, asking a child to count people who will be at dinner and then having the child use the number counted to gather enough plates is a more advanced activity than simply counting the people. The people sitting at the table provide a very clear example of the one-to-one correspondence that can be established between two sets with the same cardinal number. It is relatively easier for a child to appreciate the fact that each person has one plate than to appreciate the more abstract fact that the counting process itself establishes a one-to-one correspondence between the set being counted and the counting numbers.

In order to communicate this latter one-to-one correspondence, the child must have memorized a sequence of number names. Whether the sequence is "one, two, three"; "uno, dos, tres"; or "a, b, c," the counting process will be the same. However, when the child wishes to tell another "now many," the words used become important. Once the child has passed the "one for Daddy, one for Mommy, one for Susie, and one for me" stage he or she will need to use the counting sequence standard for the culture, and the sequence, unlike the counting task, is a product of rote learning.

Counting is a natural number-learning activity for children (Hildreth 1947) and is often encouraged by adults. For example, an aunt may sing counting songs or an uncle may ask, "How many fingers am I holding up?" Many adults do not realize there is a real difference between rote recitation of the number names and a paced recitation while pointing to individual objects one at a time. Because both are called "counting," you might have to explain to parents that the first form requires only the memorization of an ordered sequence of sounds, whereas the second requires that the number names be put into one-to-one correspondence with some set of objects. As this is done, the child must be very careful to point to each object exactly once, skipping none and repeating none. This task requires verbal and motor coordination, the use of short-term memory, and the ability to organize a response. These are not easy tasks, and mature counting behavior may take a long time to achieve.

At first children make many errors counting objects and have to be corrected often. They will gleefully count aloud to five while pointing to a group of two objects. Or they will point out only two or three objects of a group of five, not really noticing that they have not included every object. These early errors are similar to later ones made even by adults when randomly placed objects must be counted quickly. Whereas adults can become confused, forgetting what has been included previously in the count and what is yet to be counted, the child's errors result from a lack of understanding of the process rather than carelessness.

Not all authors agree that counting is the best approach to understanding number meaning. Speer and Dewey (Monroe 1917) and Stern (1949) stated flatly that arithmetic should *not* be based on counting. Cuisenaire's rods, likewise, use measurement approach to number (Figures 11–2 and 11–3, pages 98 and 99) as opposed to the "one more than" approach seen in Figures 11–1 and 11–4. Indeed, some very recent evidence suggests that some children, especially some brain-damaged or right-hemisphere-dominant children, learn better if a measurement approach is used to explain concepts of both number and place value (David-

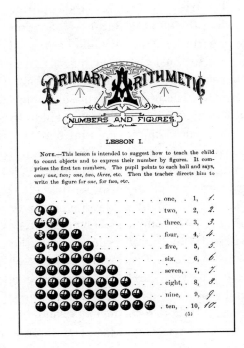

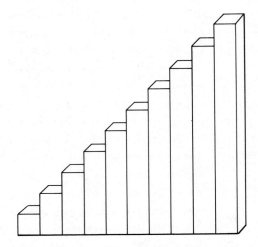

Figure 11–1   *Page from Ray's New*
Primary Arithmetic for Young Learners
by Joseph C. Ray (American Book, 1877).

Figure 11–2   *A Set of Cuisenaire Rods*

son 1979). On the other hand, some authorities, including Piaget, believe
Cuisenaire rods may confuse young children. They believe that some
children see each rod as *one* rod, focusing on a rod's unit rather than its
length, regardless of the intent of the developer, and that others ignore the
relational quality and focus on length alone rather than an understanding
of numerical relationships (Kamii and De Vries 1976).

rational counting activities

Counting remains the most usual approach to the development of the
meaning of number, and many effective strategies have been developed
over the years to make the learning task enjoyable.

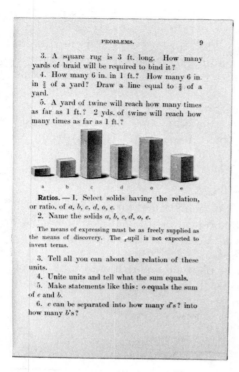

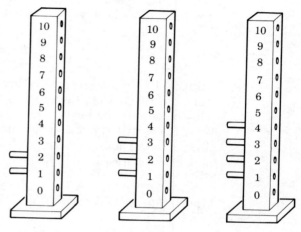

Figure 11–3 *A Measurement Approach to Number from* Speer's Arithmetics, *by William W. Speer (Ginn, 1898).*

Figure 11–4 *Counting Ladders*

Button Bowls

Collect a set of ten soft margarine bowls and tops. Slit each top. On each, write one numeral (0–9) in permanent magic marker. Provide the child with buttons and bowls with numeral indicators. If you want to provide a self-check, draw counting dots on the underside of the lids. Once the child has dropped the buttons into a bowl he or she can remove the lid, put one button on each dot, and see if there is exactly one button for each dot with no buttons left over.

My Number Book

As each number is introduced, have the child prepare a page for a number book that will be the compilation of several weeks' work. On each page the child should draw the numeral, as many objects as appropriate, and the number name. When all the numerals have been introduced, the pages can be stacked together, stapled down the left-hand side, and topped with a wallpaper or construction paper cover made by the child.

Egg Carton Counters

(1) Turn an empty Styrofoam egg carton upside down and cut slits in the "hills." Use a felt tip pen to write a numeral on each section. Provide a child with a handful of thin sticks and ask the child to place in the slot as many sticks as the numeral indicates. Label the "hills" in random order.

(2) Cut two "hills" from an egg carton. Discard them. Write one of the numerals (0–9) inside each of the remaining cups. Provide the child with a sack of beans. Ask the child to place in each cup as many beans as the numeral indicates.

Battery Board

This useful board (Figure 11–5) can be modified for any matching activity. By writing on paper rather than on the board itself you can make a very versatile device. Removable labels attached to the cup hooks will clearly identify the items to be matched.

To construct, cut a square piece of plywood and drill two columns of five (or more) holes each into it. *Beside* each hole affix a cup hook. *In* each hole place a brass brad. The items to be matched should be placed

Figure 11–5   A Battery Board

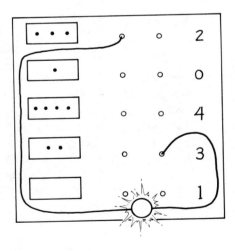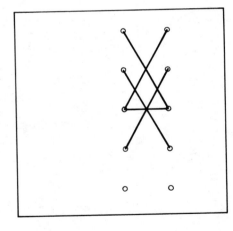

randomly on the cup hooks of each column. Now match the items on the *back* of the board by connecting one end of a wire to each corresponding brad. Attach a lightbulb and two alligator clips on wires to a battery (the lightbulb can be poked through a hole in the board). To use, attach a clip to each number of one column to its match in the other column. If the match is correct, the light will go on. If it is incorrect, the circuit will not be completed, and the light will not go on. Of course, the board may be decorated. The light might be a clown's nose or the center of a star, for example. For a change, or for work with blind children, a buzzer may be used instead of a light. Battery boards make nice presents for teachers.

Picture Matching Activities

A less dramatic matching can be done on a bulletin board or a Styrofoam meat tray. Arrange items to be matched in two columns, and attach a piece of yarn to each item in one column and a hook to each item in the other. Using the yarn, children can match each set with the numeral that answers "how many."

A similar activity can be drawn on or pasted into a file folder (Figure 11–6). Place pictures of sets of objects on one side of the folder and numerals on the other. Cover them with clear contact paper. Now children can draw the "match lines" with erasable crayon. If you use a magic marker, be careful of "bleed-through;" should this happen, cover the outside of the folder with contact or construction paper.

Figure 11–6   A File Folder Math Activity

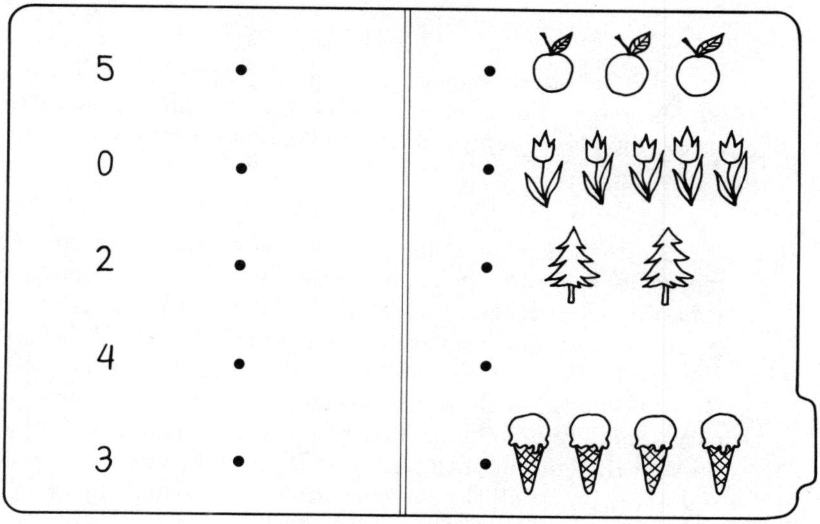

Figure 11–7   A Sorting Box

Post Office (G-rated version)

Number a set of shoeboxes from 0 to 9. Give children about fifty envelopes. Have them put as many envelopes in each box as is appropriate. A variation of this activity is to give the child a set of nine envelopes "addressed" with a picture of a set containing zero, one, two, . . . or nine objects. A commercially available partitioned sorting box such as shown in Figure 11–7 may also be used.

Circus Ponies

Choose one child as ringmaster. The rest are ponies who will prance in a circle around the ringmaster. Each pony wears a feathered headband or wristband with a numeral on it. When the ringmaster calls a number, that pony steps into the ring and stomps or whinnies the appropriate number of times.

The Bouncing Ball

Have children stand in a circle. Throw a ball to one of them and call out a number. The child should bounce the ball that many times and then throw the ball to someone else and call out a number.

Sandwich Puzzles

You will need an empty, shallow box for this activity. First cut two pieces of cardboard the same size as the box. Paste a picture on one of them, divide sections, numbered as shown in Figure 11-8a. On the other piece, color or glue a set of dots as shown in Figure 11–8b. Glue the "dot" sheet onto the top of the box. Cut the picture into pieces. To do the puzzle, the child places each numbered piece, picture side down, on the corresponding set of dots. When all the pieces have been placed, the child puts on the bottom of the box and inverts the box. This puts the picture right side up. If all the matches are correct when the child removes the top, the completed picture will be visible.

Figure 11–8a   *Pictures for the Sandwich Puzzles*

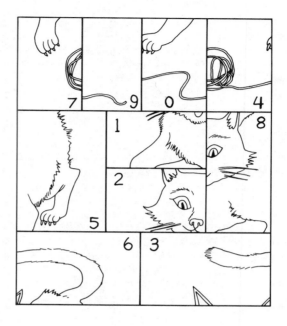

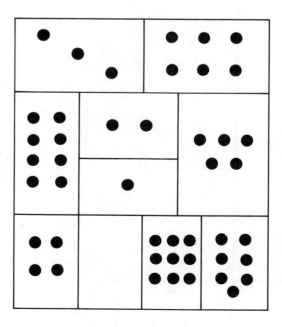

Figure 11–8b   *Dot Sets for the Sandwich Puzzles*

Number Lineup

To avoid having children associate numbers only with sets, the creative teacher uses other models. One of the most effective of these is a class-made line. Using half sheets of paper, write as many numbers as there are children in the class, one number per sheet. (Or make two or three sets of 0–10.) Give one numeral to each child. Ask the children to color the numeral and write their names on the small line at the bottom of the sheet. Place a sheet of plastic marked with equally spaced dots in an area of the classroom where the floor is relatively clear of furniture. Have each child place her or his number sheet in the appropriate position, as shown in Figure 11–9. A permanent class number line can be made by covering the whole collection of numeral cards with clear contact paper or affixing it to a clear carpet runner.

Knob Board

Screw a line of ten wooden knobs onto a block of wood. Leave enough space between them to accommodate a child's hand. Ask the students to grasp each knob and count aloud as they do so (Frostig and Maslow 1973). Numerals written on the top of each knob may aid later recognition of these symbols. A teacher wishing to use both a Cuisinaire rod approach *and* a counting approach might paint the knobs in the Cuisenaire code.

Figure 11–9   *A Walk-on Number Line*

the baratta-lorton number stations

Baratta-Lorton (1976) outlines a directed exploration of the numbers from three to ten. She suggests that number stations be set up such that up to five students may work at each station. The children work at any or all the stations, exploring each number with diverse materials. After some time has been spent in exploration of the given number, the child is encouraged to record the results of the experiments in a variety of ways as a way to connect the symbol with its real-world referent. Here is an example of a number station for *five*.

Toothpicks

Material: Boxes of flat toothpicks (cocktail toothpicks come in pretty colors).

Exploration: Have children make a variety of designs using exactly five toothpicks.

Recording: Copy or glue toothpick designs onto heavy paper or file cards. Describe the design in numerals.

Example:

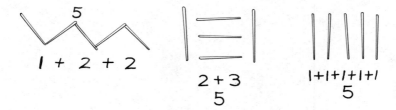

The last activity encourages the child to discuss many alternative ways to "make" five. It is hoped that talking about mathematics will be an integral part of every lesson in your classroom.

Concept Attainment According to Piaget

Table 11–1   Number concepts and approximate age range of attainment

Age	Number concept	Age	Number concept
Up to 4½ to 5	A. 1:1 correspondence is not formed accurately. No conservation of 1:1 correspondence. B. No conservation of continuous quantity (e.g., liquids); depends on size and shape of container. C. No conservation of discontinuous quantity (e.g., beads); depends on size and shape of container. D. Inability to seriate; no conservation of serial correspondence. E. No formation of conservation of ordinal correspondence. F. No understanding of cardinal number, ordinal number, or unit. G. Nonexistence of part-whole relations; the whole is destroyed when divided into parts. H. Addition of sets of objects; one object plus seven objects does not equal four objects plus four objects; there are more in the former sum. I. Transitivity of 1:1 correspondence; that set X is equivalent to set Y and set Y is equivalent to set Z does not imply that set X is equivalent to set Z. J. Multiplication property of 1:1 correspondence; if set X is equivalent to set Z and set Y is equivalent to set Z, then set XUY is equivalent to set 2Z.	5 to 6	C. Gradual awareness of conservation of discontinuous quantity. D. Trial-and-error seriation; no conservation of serial correspondence. E. No ordinal correspondence. F. Gradual awareness of cardinal number, ordinal number, and unit. G. Intuitive trial-and-error understanding of part-whole relations. H. Gradual awareness of addition of sets of objects. I. Gradual awareness of transitivity of 1:1 correspondence. J. Gradual awareness of multiplication property of 1:1 correspondence.
5 to 6	A. 1:1 correspondence constructed but not conserved. B. Gradual awareness of conservation of continuous quantity.	6 to 7½	A. Conservation of continuous quantity. # B. Conservation of continuous quantity. # C. Conservation of discontinuous quantity. # D. Seriation and conservation of serial correspondence. # E. Realization of ordinal correspondence. # F. Cardinal number, ordinal number, and unit understood. # G. Immediate grasp of part-whole relations. # H. Immediate grasp of addition of sets of objects. # I. Immediate grasp of transitivity of 1:1 correspondence. # J. Immediate grasp of multiplication property of 1:1 correspondence. #

The symbol **#** means the final attainment of a concept was reached by the children.

(From Coxford 1963, 420)

Table 11–2   Two- and three-dimensional measurement concepts and approximate age range of attainment

Age*	Measurement concept	Age	Measurement concept
Up to 6	A. No conservation of area. B. No conservation of complementary area. C. No measurement of area with units of area. D. Trial-and-error division of area. E. Only a slight increase in size when trying to double an area or volume while keeping the same shape (a square or a cube). F. No conservation of volume; volume judged by longest linear dimension.	7 to 8	E. Doubles all dimensions or makes dissimilar figure. F. Conservation of interior volume (amount held).
6 or 7	A. Conservation of area only after trial and error. C. All units treated as equivalent whether they are or not. D. Halving done.	8 to 10	B. Conservation of complementary ara. # C. Measurement of areas with units of area (unit iteration). # D. Dividing into fifths and sixths is done. # E. The relation between edges and area or volume is found by trial and error.
7 to 8	A. Conservation of area. # B. Conservation of complementary area only when similar parts are covered. D. Dividing into thirds done.	11 or 12	E. Multiplicative relation between length and area or volume is understood; it is influenced by schooling. # F. Conservation of true volume measurement with units of volume. #

The symbol # means the final attainment of a concept was reached by the children.

*   When a letter is omitted in an age range, the development is at the same stage as in the previous age range.

(From Coxford 1963, 423)

Table 11–3   Measurement concepts and approximate age range of attainment

Age*	Measurement concept	Age	Measurement concept
Up to 4½	A. Visual transfer of lengths (they look the same). B. No conservation of distance (measure of empty space). C. Length (measure of occupied space) determined by endpoints. D. No conservation of length. E. Inability to measure; i.e., no use of iterate units. F. Visual estimate to locate a point in two or three dimensions. G. Inability to subdivide two line segments equally.	7 to 8	A. Transfer by means of an object (independent of the body) longer or the same length as the object to be measured. Transitivity of length—mean age 7½. B. Conservation of distance symmetry (AB=BA). # D. Conservation of length— one-half of those 7 to 7½ and three-quarters of those 7½ to 8½. # F. Realization of need for two or three measurements in locating points yet no coordination of length, width, and height. G. Accurate subdivision of line segments.
4½ or 5 to 6	A. Visual transfer augmented by manual transfer (bringing objects closer together).		
6 to 7	A. Body transfer of lengths (a third term introduced). B. Occasional conservation of distance. C. Length no longer determined by endpoints but by configuration of material between the endpoints. # D. Gradual awareness of conservation of length. E. Trial-and-error measurement and inconsistent use of units. F. Use of rulers to aid visual estimates. G. Trial-and-error subdivision of line segments.	8 to 9	A. Operation measurement; i.e., use of rules shorter than the object and unit iteration. # E. Unit iteration and accurate measurement—mean age 8 to 8½. # G. Use of measurement to check on accurate subdivision of line segments. #
		9 to 10	F. Use of two or three perpendicular measurements to locate a point—mean age 9 to 9½. #

The symbol **#** means the final attainment of a concept was reached by the children.

*   When a letter is omitted in an age range, the development is at the same stage as in the previous age range.

(From Coxford 1963, 425)

twelve

vocabulary development

From their study of teaching reading and language arts, teachers know techniques appropriate for the teaching of new words. Like reading vocabulary, mathematics vocabulary must be built. The list on pages 110 and 111 gives some words that are useful in the spoken mathematics vocabulary of kindergarten and first-grade students. These words will later become part of the students' written vocabulary as well.

The use of sets and terms such as *one-to-one correspondence* is not new. During the 1960s and 1970s, however, the mathematical language used in children's tests, school district curriculum guides, standardized tests, professional meetings, and methods tests for teachers was extremely precise. Experience has shown us that two-early formalism is not only unnecessary but that children may revert to rote memorization if it is forced upon them. Keep the language clear but informal.

technical problems

Because our culture uses different words to tell how many or how much and to tell position or rank, children must become familiar with two different kinds of numbers—cardinal (which build on concepts of classification) and ordinal (which build on concepts of seriation). Cardinal numbers tell quantity (one, two, etc.); ordinal numbers tell position (first, seecond, etc.). It is important that the teacher use correct forms to indicate position and to help children connect these with the cardinal numbers. This is not something that happens automatically. (A third use of number, say in the telephone directory, implies neither meaning.) As far as young children are concerned, it is enough to expose them to the number words by using them to indicate position or numerousness. Thorough understanding of the terms will be hastened by corrected practice and, as with other grammatical conventions, by hearing adults use them correctly.

Older children must learn many technical terms (Appendix C). Although teaching children these words does not increase their understanding or skill, knowing the correct terminology can be very practical during

A Basic Word List

Quantity		Capacity	Number	Geometry	Measurement	
all	least	empty	count	angle	balance	longer
amount	less	full	eighth	circle	big	longest
another	many	hold	fifth	cone	bigger	measure
as few as	more	less	first	cube	biggest	meter
as many as	most	measure	fourth	curved	centimeter	meterstick
both	much	more	ninth	line	cup	pint
different	none		nothing	rectangle	even	pound
dozen	one-fourth		once	round	feet	quart
each	one-half		second	sphere	foot	ruler
enough	one-third		seventh	square	gallon	scale
equal	pair		sixth	straight	gram	small
every	part		tens	triangle	heavier	smaller
few	rest		tenth		heaviest	smallest
fewer	same		third		heavy	tall
fewest	several		twice		inch	taller
fraction	single		zero		large	tallest
group	some				larger	tiny
half	whole				largest	thick
					length	thin
					light	weigh
					lighter	weight
					lightest	wide
					liter	width
					little	yard
					long	yardstick

class discussions of the various operations, applications, and algorithms. It is awkward and sometimes confusing to have to refer to the sum as the "number you get when you add" or the dividend as the "number that is being divided up." Vocabulary development should take second place to concept development, but second place does not mean omission.

Children should have many conversations about measurement and numbers before they are confronted with formal situations. This does not imply that the teacher's planning with respect to vocabulary development is haphazard. To the contrary, the teacher must prepare an environment in which mathematical situations requiring discussion are heeded.

A Basic Word List

Operation	Money	Time		Space		Temperature
add	bought	after	now	above	last	cool
addition	buy	afternoon	old	back	left	cold
altogether	cent	before	older	below	middle	fall
answer	change	day	overnight	beside	on	hot
correct	cost	early	second	between	out	spring
divide	dime	fast	slow	close	outside	summer
double	dollar	faster	slower	down	over	warm
fact	nickel	half hour	slowest	edge	right	winter
how many	penny	hour	soon	front	space	
how much	price	instant	tomorrow	here	there	
multiply	quarter	late	until	in	top	
share	spend	later	week	inside	up	
subtract		latest	when			
sum		lunchtime	year			
table		minute	yesterday			
together		month	young			
		next	younger			
		noon	youngest			

thirteen

individual assessment techniques

During the primary years, testing for attainment of prenumber, early number, and measurement concepts provides useful data for instruction and grouping students. An informal testing device is shown in Figures 13–1 and 13–2 (pages 114–118). The latter assessment instrument was adapted from Hollister and Gunderson (1954). Either can be modified by the teacher to fit a particular child or classroom.

For information on the children's present level of functioning, the teacher can administer Piagetian conservation tasks, especially those of number, length, and mass. Directions for these tasks are given in Figure 13–3 (pages 119–121). Instruction in mathematics need not be postponed until all these tasks are mastered. Their contribution is to alert the teacher to possible areas of misunderstanding on the part of the students and to reconvince teachers that children are ruled by their perceptions in ways very different from the way adults generally are.

the idea of diagnosis

Children in the early-childhood classroom often display abilities far ahead or far behind what the teacher has come to expect. In such cases, the teacher's diagnostic skills will be called into play in order to meet the special needs of a child. Skill in diagnosis is part science and part art and cannot be described in any comprehensive fashion in this brief treatment. For more information, please consult books on the subject (for example, Ashlock 1981) or take courses in this area. All that will be attempted here is to acquaint you with the fact that such an area of study exists and that it is of value in the regular classroom as well as in special settings.

The diagnostic approach centers on the individual and that individual's interaction with a specific portion of the content of elementary school mathematics. If you keep both of those descriptors in mind, you will be able to conceptualize any particular diagnostic incident in a manner that will help you meet individual needs.

The tools of diagnosis may be standardized tests, teacher-made instruments, or a clinical interview. Even more important than the tools, however, is the atmosphere in which the diagnosis takes place. The idea of the diagnostic endeavor is to find out what the child knows and does not know and on what level the knowledge is secure. In order for the child to perform well, he or she must be put at ease—and the teacher must be at ease also. The diagnostic session is not the time to teach the content under consideration—and it is definitely not the time to show annoyance at the fact that the student hasn't learned it. The session should be used to gather information; reteaching should take place later.

Although there are many standardized tests in the area of reading, there are fewer in the area of mathematics, and even those that exist are in one significant way unsatisfactory. It is important in mathematics to discern if the child has a complete understanding at all levels—concrete, pictorial, and abstract—for each of the concepts being probed. Pencil-and-paper tests can assess at most the latter two levels; therefore, the teacher seeking accurate diagnosis of a child's strengths and weaknesses must supplement tests with experiences using concrete materials. Situations parallel to those on the tests should be posed, and the child should be asked to demonstrate the operation with buttons, shells, or some other attractive objects.

Of the available tests, KeyMath (American Guidance Service, Publisher's Building, Circle Pines, Minnesota 55014) is perhaps the most satisfactory for children in grades one to four. It is easy to administer and score, inexpensive (once the initial kit is purchased), and relatively easy to interpret, even for those who are unfamiliar with the test. An hour with the KeyMath manual will be sufficient for you to give and interpret the test. Note that the manual's authors urge the tester to set up a comfortable testing environment. Don't forget that—it *is* important.

Figure 13–1

AN INDIVIDUAL MATHEMATICS READINESS INVENTORY/PART I
PRENUMBER

Pupil_____Grade_____Date_____C.A._____

A. Classification	B. Seriation	C. Patterning
1. According to color_____	1. Shortest to tallest (1 set)_____	1. R B R B R B_____
2. According to shape_____	2. Shortest to tallest (2 sets)_____	2. R B B R B B R B B_____
3. According to size_____	3. Reverse order_____	
4. With two attributes_____		
5. According to number_____		

DIRECTIONS FOR INDIVIDUAL MATHEMATICAL READINESS INVENTORY: PART I

A. <u>Classification</u>

1. <u>According to color.</u> Present a set of materials so that each of three shapes is available in three colors and two sizes. Ask the child to put all the red ones in one pile, all the green ones in another pile, and all the blue ones in a third pile.

2. <u>According to shape.</u> Using the same set, ask the child to put the circles together, the triangles together, and the squares together in three separate piles.

3. <u>According to size.</u> Ask the child to put the large pieces in one pile and the small pieces in another.

4. <u>With two attributes.</u> Ask the child to put all the large blue pieces in one pile and all the small red ones in another.

5. <u>According to number.</u> Make three sets of two objects, three sets of three objects, and three sets of four objects. Ask the child to point to all the sets that have the same number of things as the set you point to.

B. <u>Seriation</u>

1. <u>Shortest to tallest (1 set).</u> Give the child a set of five objects, differing in height only. Say, "Please put these in order from smallest to tallest." (Use other words if the child does not understand.)

2. <u>Shortest to tallest (2 sets).</u> Present two sets of five objects that vary proportionately. Ask the child to put them in order so that the littlest one of the first set goes with the littlest one of the other set. Hats and cowboys, canes and dolls, and bats and balls are some items that might be so seriated.

Figure 13–1   *(cont'd)*

    3. <u>Reverse order.</u> Seriate a set of five straws. Give the child a second set to seriate in the <u>reverse</u> order.

C. <u>Patterning</u>

    1. <u>R B R B R B.</u> Make a train of blocks, alternating red and blue blocks. Ask the child to continue the train in the same way.

    2. <u>R B B R B B R B B.</u> Make a train using the pattern red, blue, blue.

Figure 13–2

AN INDIVIDUAL MATHEMATICS READINESS INVENTORY/PART II

Pupil_____Grade_____Date_____C.A._____

A. Number

    1. Ability to count
        a. Rote   1st trial_____   2nd trial_____
        b. Rational   1st trial_____   2nd trial_____

    2. Ability to recognize number quantities

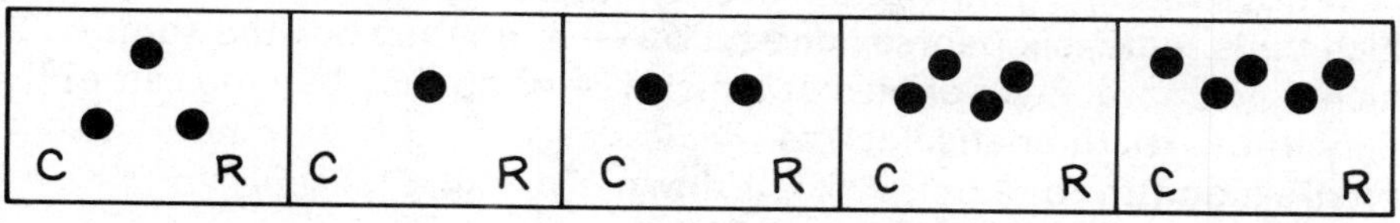

    ( )   ( )   ( )   ( )   ( )

    3. Ability to select a designated number group

    (3)   (1)   (2)   (5)   (4)

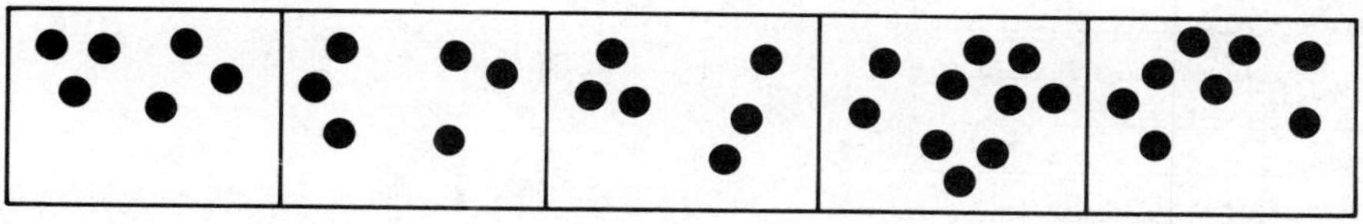

    ( )   ( )   ( )   ( )   ( )

    4. Ability to match number symbols

2	3	1	7	0
5	9	6	4	8

Figure 13–2   *(cont'd)*

5. Ability to recognize number symbols

	4	5	3	1	2	7	6	8	9	0
1st trial	( )	( )	( )	( )	( )	( )	( )	( )	( )	( )
	3	0	2	5	1	6	8	9	7	4
2nd trial	( )	( )	( )	( )	( )	( )	( )	( )	( )	( )

6. Ability to put nine numeral cards in sequence

___   ___   ___   ___   ___   ___   ___   ___   ___   ___

7. Ability to match a numeral to a set

Correct responses:	0	1	2	3	4	5	6	7	8	9
	( )	( )	( )	( )	( )	( )	( )	( )	( )	( )

B. Geometry and Measurement

   8. Ability to select a geometric shape

     Circle_____ ( )   Square_____ ( )

     Rectangle_____ ( )   Triangle_____ ( )

   9. Ability to recognize the value of coins

     What is this coin? (penny)

     What is this coin? (nickel)

     What is this coin? (dime)

     Which buys more, a penny or a nickel — or do they buy the same?

     Which buys more, six pennies or a nickel — or do they buy the same?

     Which buys more, five pennies or a nickel — or do they buy the same?

  10. Ability to use mathematical terms

     1. First/second/third   5. Up/down

     2. Inside/outside   6. Older/younger

     3. Over/under   7. More/less

     4. Taller/shorter   8. Over/under/on

C. Conservation Tasks

   Number (4)_____(7)_____

   Length (—)_____

      (~)_____

   Mass_____

   Volume_____

   Class inclusion_____

COMMENTS:

Figure 13–2   *(cont'd)*

DIRECTIONS FOR INDIVIDUAL MATHEMATICS READINESS INVENTORY/PART II

A. Number

1. <u>Ability to count.</u> Present ten objects such as blocks or beans. Since the ability to do rational counting also implies the ability to count by rote, test the former first. Ask the child, "Can you count the number blocks on the table? You may touch them with your fingers as you count." If he or she loses the one-to-one correspondence before arriving at ten, record the last number in correct association. Remove the counters and then say, "I'd like to hear you count as far as you can." Record the last number said in proper sequence. If there is any reason to believe that the pupil can count better than he or she demonstrated on the first trial, repeat the test. If the child counts past 30, you may want to suggest he or she stop counting.

2. <u>Ability to recognize number quantities.</u> Present the beads as shown in each box, one box at a time. Ask, "How many counters do you see?" If the child counts to find the answer, circle C on the record sheet. If it appears that he or she had an immediate recognition of the set, circle R. Record the incorrect responses in the parentheses below each box.

3. <u>Ability to select a designated number group.</u> Arrange the counters as shown in the first box. Then say, "Give me three counters." If the child reaches for a set of three with little hesitation, circle G to indicate that she or he appeared to use a knowledge of grouping in making the selection. If she or he counts to find the set of three, circle C. Record an erroneous response in the parentheses below the box. Repeat this procedure for each of the remaining four boxes. The number of counters to ask for is given in parentheses above the box.

4. <u>Ability to match number symbols.</u> Put a card with numbered spaces on it on the table. Also place on the table nine squares, each with one numeral on it. Say, "Let's see if you can put this number (pointing to one of the small squares) over the same number on the big card." In a similar way, ask the child to cover each of the numerals. Record any mismatches with an X on the response sheet block for that numeral.

5. <u>Ability to recognize number symbols.</u> Using the same numeral cards as in test item 4, ask, "Can you point to the four?" Note the numerals the child apparently confuses or fails to recognize by writing the incorrect selection below the numeral called for. If you feel the child will do better on a second trial, repeat the test.

Figure 13–2   *(cont'd)*(Items 1–5 adapted from Hollister and Gunderson, 1954, 24–27)

6. <u>Ability to put nine numeral cards in sequence.</u> Using the same numeral cards as in test item 4, ask the child to make a train starting with one. Record the child's response. Repeat if necessary.

7. <u>Ability to match a numeral to a set.</u> Present a set of six cards: one card with one dot, one with two dots, one with three dots, one with four dots, one with five dots, and one with six dots. Using the numeral cards from test item 4, and ask the child to put the card that tells how many next to each card with dots. Circle the numerals correctly matched on the response sheet. Record incorrect responses in the parentheses below the number.

B. Geometry and Measurement

8. <u>Ability to select a geometric shape.</u> Spread out on the table several geometric shapes. Ask the child to give in turn a circle, a rectangle, a square, and a triangle. Decide each correct response. Record incorrect responses in the parentheses beside the item.

9. <u>Ability to recognize the value of coins.</u> On a response sheet record the child's answers to the questions given. Use real money in this assessment.

10. <u>Ability to use mathematical terms.</u> Prepare a picture file to use as you ask the following questions. Circle correct responses on the child's response sheet.

1. Which____is first in line?	6. Which____is over the____?
2. Which____is second?	7. Which____is under the____?
3. Which____is third?	8. Which____is taller?
4. Which____is inside?	9. Which____is shorter?
5. Which____is outside?	10. Which____is up?
11. Which____is down?	15. Which____has more?
12. Which____is older?	16. Which____is under the____?
13. Which____is younger?	17. Which____is over the____?
14. Which____has less?	18. Which____is on the____?

C. Conservation Tasks

For items in this category, consult any standard description of Piagetian tasks or Figure 13–3.

Figure 13–3

SOME TESTS FOR ASSESSING COGNITIVE LEVEL

A. Number
  1. <u>One-to-one correspondence</u>
     Materials: 19 marbles, 2 clear drinking glasses
     Directions: Place the glasses directly in front of the child. Drop marbles one at one at the same time from each hand into each glass. When you have seven marbles left, say to the child, "Watch me now," and drop three marbles into your glass, and none into the child's. Now drop the four remaining marbles into the two glasses as before.
          Ask the child, "Are there more marbles in my glass or in your glass, or do they have the same?"
  2. <u>Continuous quantity</u>
     Materials: 2 drinking glasses of the same size; 1 tall, thin container; colored liquid
     Directions: Pour equal amounts of liquid into each of the glasses. Ask the child if there is the same amount in each glass. If the child says there is, continue the experiment. If the child says there is not, adjust the amount of liquid until the child is satisfied each glass holds the same amount of liquid.
          Now pour the liquid from one of the glasses into the other container. Ask the child, "Is there more here (indicate one container) or here (indicate the glass), or are they the same?"
     Variation 1: Instead of one tall thin container, use three small containers.
     Variation 2: Use five small containers.
  3. <u>Discontinuous quantity</u>
     Materials: 20 marbles, 2 clear drinking glasses, 1 small cake pan
     Directions: Place ten marbles in each glass, counting as you go and placing them in the glasses together.
          Ask the child, "Are there more marbles in this glass (point to one) or in this (point to the other), or are they the same?" If the child says they have the same amount, pour the contents of one of the glasses into the pan. Now ask, "Are there more here (point to the pan) or here (point to the glass), or are they the same?"
  4. <u>Seriation</u>
     Materials: 10 drinking straws, cut to 10 different lengths
     Directions: (1) Give the child three of the straws. Ask the child to put them in order from shortest to longest. (Use straws 1, 5, and 8). Give the child three more straws (2, 7, and 9). Repeat the instruction. Now ask the child to make one staircase with all six

Figure 13–3   *(cont'd)*

straws. (2) Give the child all ten straws. Ask him or her to put them in order from shortest to longest.

5. Number conservation
   a. Materials: 8 poker chips, blocks, or candies identical in size
      Directions: Place the items in two equally spaced rows. Ask the child, "Are there more in this row (point to one row) or this row (point to the other), or are there the same in each row?" Spread out one of the rows. Repeat the question.
   b. Materials: 16 disks, blocks, or pieces of candy of identical size
      Directions: Make two rows of eight objects. Have the child affirm that the rows have an equal number of items. Now bunch one row into a group of seven and a single object, the other row into two groups of four objects. Ask the child if there are more in one row than the other or if the rows have the same amount.

6. Part-whole conservation
   Materials: 2 square crackers
   Directions: Place the crackers on the table. Ask the child, "Is there more to eat with this cracker (point to one of them) or this cracker (point to the other), or is there the same?"
   Break one of the crackers into several small pieces. Repeat the question.

B. Measurement
   1. Distance
      Materials: 2 plastic animals or cars and a divider
      Directions: Place the two objects about arm's length apart. Ask the child if they are near to or far from each other.
      a. Place the divider midway between them. Now, using the child's answer, say, "Are they as (near, far) now?"
      b. Ask the child, "Is this farther (move finger from the right-hand object to the left-hand object) or this (move finger in opposite direction), or are they the same?

   2. Length
      a. Materials: 2 Popsicle sticks or new unsharpened pencils
         Directions: Place the sticks parallel so that the ends are even. Ask the child if they are the same length or if one stick is longer. Slide one stick forward. Repeat the question.
         Place the sticks at right angles. Repeat the question.
      b. Materials: 2 pieces of yarn the same length
         Directions: Stretch out the pieces of yarn side by side on the table. Ask the child if they are the same length. Take one piece of yarn and make it seem shorter by making "hills and valleys" with it. Repeat the question.

   3. Area
      Materials: 2 identical pieces of paper or felt, 12 blocks, 2 small plastic cows

Figure 13–3　　　*(cont'd)*

Directions: Place the two pieces of felt (green is especially appropriate) on the table, telling the child that these are fields of grass; one belongs to the child, and one to you. Put a cow on each field.

Now put one block on each field, telling the child that the block represents a barn. Ask the child if one cow has more grass to eat or if they have the same amount. Add a second block to each field. In one field, put the second block touching the first; in the other field, put it at some distance from the first. Repeat the question. Add the rest of the blocks in the same way so that one field has a single large barn and the other six small, scattered barns. Repeat the question.

4. Mass

Materials: modeling clay or dough
Directions: Roll the clay into two balls that the child will say are the same size.

a. Roll one of the balls into a sausage shape. Ask the child, "Is there more clay here (indicate the ball) or here (indicate the sausage), or are they the same?"

b. Roll the clay into two balls again. When the child asserts they have the same amount of clay, break one of the balls into three smaller balls. Repeat the question.

5. Weight

Follow the directions for test item 4, but ask, "Does this weigh more or does this, or do they weigh the same?"

C. Set Inclusion

Materials: 8 brown wooden blocks, 2 red wooden blocks
Directions: Ask the child what the brown beads are made of. Then ask the child what the red blocks are made of. Then ask, "Are there more brown blocks or more wooden blocks?"

Addition	Subtraction	Multiplication	Division
1. Counting	1. Counting	1. Counting	1. Counting
2. Sets	2. Inverse of addition	2. Repeated addition	2. Repeated subtraction
3. Number line	3. Sets	3. Sets	3. Inverse of multiplication
4. Balance beam	4. Number line	4. Number line	4. Sets
	5. Balance beam	5. Balance beam	5. Number line
		6. Arrays	6. Balance beam
		7. Cross products of sets	7. Arrays
			8. Cross products of sets

Other commercial tests that might be useful at the preschool and primary levels are the Mann-Suiter Developmental Arithmetic Inventory (Allyn and Bacon), The Kraner Preschool Math Inventory (Learning Concepts, 2501 N. Lamar Street, Austin, Texas 78705), The Iowa Test of Preschool Development (GO-MO, 1906 Main Street, Cedar Falls, Iowa 50613) and The Arithmetic Readiness Inventory (Merrill). A test that gives only one item of each type at the symbolic level is *not* a diagnostic test according to contemporary definitions, and the results of the test should be probed in more detail if valid individual education plans are to be developed.

Many school districts and most commercial mathematics programs have a set of behavioral objectives that can form the basis for teacher-made diagnostic instruments. Again, it is essential to test the child on all relevant levels. Do *not* assume that because he or she can manipulate the figures or recite the number facts a solid understanding of an operation has been attained. Many of your colleagues can serve as models of people who can divide a fraction by a fraction but can tell you neither why they are performing the steps nor what a pictorial or concrete analogue of them would look like. When you construct a teacher-made test, do remember that you cannot test for *all* the material at once. Details on the construction of diagnostic tests can be found in chapters 10 and 14 of Underhill (1977).

The best-known model for the clinical interview is the work of the Swiss genetic epistomologist Jean Piaget. The foremost individual diagnostician in this country was also one of its first—William Brownell. He, like the more famous Piaget, devoted a lifetime to developing procedures that would help professionals understand how children learn. Brownell developed his procedures in school-like settings; they are still applicable to the schoolrooms of today, some forty years later. Writing at the same time, Leo J. Brueckner developed a classification of arithmetic skills very similar to that later encouraged by Gagné. The teacher who attempts clinical interactive interviews joins a fine tradition indeed.

The rules suggested by Brownell (1941) for successful interviews with children have stood the test of time and are worth your consideration.

1.   Avoid cues and leading questions.
2.   Do not be satisfied with superficial answers to questions; probe.
3.   Set the pace of the interview at a level comfortable for the child.
4.   When responses are ambiguous, vary the question in order to draw the child out.

5. Maintain a friendly, pleasant atmosphere.
6. Terminate the interview when the child shows signs of restlessness, anxiety, or boredom.
7. Record the child's answers verbatim whenever possible.

The material around which the clinical interview is conducted can be the same as that found on a standardized or teacher-made test. The difference is in the administration of the items. In the clinical interview the child's answers give direction to the next question, which is often an exploration of the previous question. Clinical interviews take time— perhaps up to an hour—but they yield valuable data for classroom planning. They can be especially valuable when IEP's must be constructed for children with special needs, as required under PL 94 –142.

considerations concerning remediation

Once the diagnostic tests have been administered and the results studied, a course of remediation should be charted. Techniques for specific diagnosed difficulties and challenging material for the gifted student are suggested in many readily available publications, so for the present we will consider merely the process of individualization—where can you begin to help a child? First you will want to set up some type of record-keeping system. Many teachers find that individual file folders labeled with the children's names are convenient storage places for testing results and individual educational plans; the folders themselves are also easily stored in shelf files especially made for that purpose or in contact paper covered detergent boxes. Second, when a child has many diagnosed difficulties, the teacher must draw up a priority listing and decide which to work on first. Concentrating on one problem at a time is more apt to lead to success than fragmenting the attention of both teacher and child. This is *not* a suggestion to spend thirty minutes daily drilling on the number facts—a few minutes a day is enough for that—but when concept development is at stake, a superfluity of new material is bound to lead to mental indigestion, a condition that should be avoided at all costs. Third, setting a good emotional tone to the meeting is vital. Patience, good humor, patience, creative presentation of remedial material, patience and encouragement—all are necessary. Oh yes, and, of course, patience.

Some special guidelines might help the teacher or other adult who is working with a child needing special attention in mathematics, either because the child has missed lessons due to illness or a mobile family, because the child is slower to conceptualize the material than the rest of the class, or because the child has some physical or perceptual problem that hinders learning. Here are some starters to consider.

1.   Be sure the goals of the instruction are clear to both you and the child and to any other adults who are working with the child.

2.   Allow—indeed, encourage—the child to use his or her own language in the answering of questions or the explanation of operations.

3.   Encourage the child to assess his or her own progress and to acknowledge every gain.

4.   When facts are to be learned, include *brief* frequent drill in your sessions. Make the drill interesting.

5.   When concepts are to be discovered, use a variety of materials and allow the child time to think about what he or she is doing with the materials. Encourage (but do not force) verbalization.

6.   Give immediate positive feedback whenever the child answers correctly. "That's good" is a balm to the sore spirit.

7.   Use strategies and approaches that are new to the child and to the classroom. The child may be able to show someone else what he or she has learned in a way that will be a learning experience for everyone.

8.   Help the child mentally organize the material you are presenting so connections can be formed between old and new learnings. Suggest (but do not force) an accepted conceptual structure.

9.   Allow the child choices, whenever they are possible. Even such small choices as "Would you like to use the felt tip pen or write on the chalkboard today?" give the child some control over the learning situations. We all feel less anxious when we have as much control as we can handle comfortably.

10.   Keep the working time light in tone but on task. Research has shown what most of us intuitively believe—when children stay on task, they learn more.

fourteen

two elementary operations: addition and subtraction

Many people think that the most important aspect of mathematics a child can learn is how to add, subtract, multiply, and divide rapidly and accurately; some would assert that the entire mathematics program at every level should revolve around that aim. Research as well as reasoned thinking, however, has shown that the ability to compute well does not guarantee the ability to choose which computations need to be done in a problem-solving situation. Children who learn to become efficient symbol pushers but who fail to develop meanings for the symbols they are writing become stunted in their mathematical growth. This fact becomes painfully obvious when these unfortunate children study addition and subtraction with regrouping in the second grade.

According to Piaget, children must work through procedures of adding and subtracting before processing the symbols $3 + 5 = $ _____ acquire any meaning. We cannot give these meanings to children by merely repeating the answers, although we can train children to answer "eight" when we ask "three plus five equals what?" in a fashion similar to training toddlers to say "moo" when we ask "what can a cow say?" Neither answer should be assumed to be more than a rote reponse to a repeated and rewarded stimulus. Mary Baratta-Lorton (1976) in a mathematics curriculum exemplary for its concern for both mathematical correctness and young children's needs and abilities has developed a set of activities or games designed to help promote an understanding of these most important foundational operations. As in all appropriate mathematical instruction with young children, manipulation of real objects is the first step, which is then followed by extensive talking about what was done with fellow students and with the teacher. The next step is drawing or describing pictures that record the action. Later, symbols can be introduced—at first along with the pictures, and then alone.

For each of the four fundamental operations, there are several possible explanations (Burton and Knifong 1980, 1983; Knifong and Burton in press(b)). Each one suggests a particular way to look at these abstract concepts by linking the mathematical operation to familiar objects or actions. In order for children to construct a complete understanding of addition, for example, they must be exposed to all the explanations of addition. This exposure is best accomplished by providing students opportunities to consider a variety of short stories using numbers and lengths to act out their solutions, to talk about what was done, and to record their experiences in a way meaningful to them.

For addition, four models are possible: counting, sets, the number line, and the balance beam. These same approaches, plus one more—the inverse of addition—can be used to teach subtraction. These plus other models are used to explain multiplication and division. (See Figure 14–1) Because children will be expected to recognize and use each of these models in problems, it is important that all of them be included in practice situations presented to and generated by the students.

Figure 14–1   *Models for the Fundamental Binary Operations*

Addition	Subtraction	Multiplication	Division
1. Counting	1. Counting	1. Counting	1. Counting
2. Sets	2. Inverse of addition	2. Repeated addition	2. Repeated subtraction
3. Number line	3. Sets	3. Sets	3. Inverse of multiplication
4. Balance beam	4. Number line	4. Number line	4. Sets
	5. Balance beam	5. Balance beam	5. Number line
		6. Arrays	6. Balance beam
		7. Cross products of sets	7. Arrays
			8. Cross products of sets

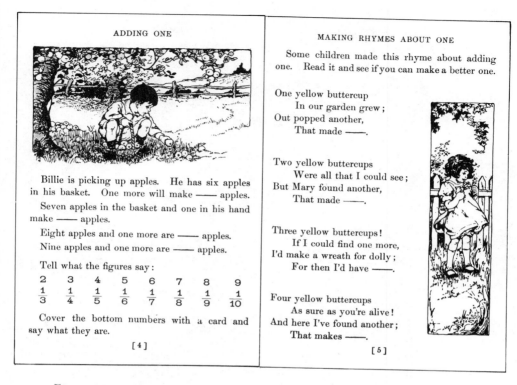

Figure 14–2   *Pages from* A Child's Book of Numbers for First and Second Grades *by John C. Stone (Benjamin H. Sanborn, 1930).*

models for addition

counting

Addition is a binary operation. This means that two numbers (addends) must be chosen before one can find the value of the operation (the sum). Counting, on the other hand, is a unary (from the Latin root meaning one) operation. To count, a beginning place is all we need to perform the operation correctly.

One continually popular way to explain addition is to use counting (Figure 14–2). For many children, this is an explanation they have figured out for themselves, using a very "handy" counter (Ginsburg 1977). To find $2 + 3 =$ _____, one would say "one, two," then "one, two, three," then "one, two, three, four, five." The last number is recognized as the sum. Chisanbop and Fingermath also use the counting approach, though the fingers are used in a way different from the traditional untutored style.

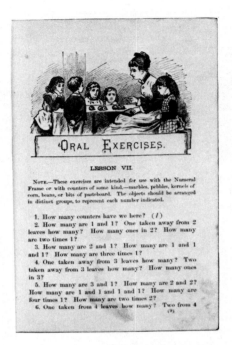

Figure 14–3   *Page from* Ray's New Primary Arithmetic for Young Learners *by Joseph C. Ray (American Book, 1877).*

Counting is a sure-fire method of getting the answer of addition examples—counting always works. It is sometimes, however, far from the most efficient method. Try adding 67 and 49 by counting!

As a process for finding the answer to "How many in all?", counting with objects also has a long history (Figure 14–3). Whether or not the practice is discouraged, pupils perennially act on and often explicitly state the axiom "When in doubt, count." In the face of stern reproaches and physical punishment, children have counted on their fingers under their desktops, under their chairs, or in their pockets. When counting on fingers was strictly forbidden, children counted their teeth with their tongues, made quiet taps with their feet, or drew imaginary dots in the air. Despite this persistence, counting—especially on the fingers—continues to annoy teachers. "How can I get them to stop counting on their fingers?" is a frequent question. Finger counting is normal until the end of grade two but will persist until the number facts are learned at the immediate recall level. If you don't want fingercounters, see that students memorize the facts.

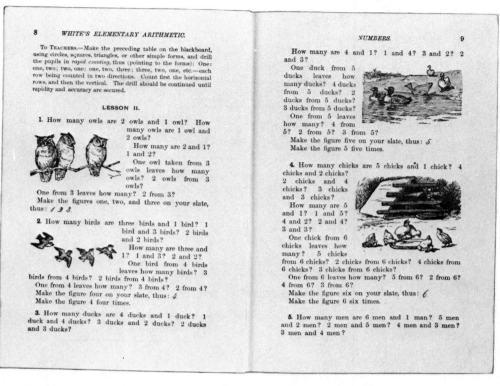

Figure 14–4   Pages from White's Elementary Arithmetic *by E. E. White (American Book, 1911).*

sets

Sets was the popular word in the "new mathematics" of the mid-1960s. In a less formal fashion, the set approach is one of the oldest and most widely used explanations for whole-number operators. (See Figures 14–4 (above), 14–5 and 14–6 (pages 128 and 129), and Baratta-Lorton 1979). *The* method during the 1800s, it has enjoyed continued popularity to the present day. "John has two apples and Mary gave him three more . . ." was as familiar a situation to our great-grandparents as it is to us. In this model, the number sentence $2 + 3 =$ _____ suggests that a group of two elements (not necessarily apples) is joined to a group of three elements, and the task is to find out how many there are after this joining happens. Children can use many objects to illustrate number stories involving groups—beans, pretty macaroni*, buttons, seeds, nuts, keys, and blocks

---

*   Place uncooked macaroni of a variety of shapes in a glass or stainless steel bowl with food color and two drops of alcohol or vinegar. Wearing a plastic bag on your hand, toss the macaroni in the coloring solution. Remove and let the noodles dry on wax paper. (This recipe was adapted from one at a *Mathematics Their Way* workshop; its origin is unknown.)

Figure 14—5   Page from Elementary School Mathematics *second edition, by Robert E. Eicholz (Addison-Wesley, 1968).*

are a few of the most common. As children make up problems and work them out with a wide variety of materials, this concept becomes meaningful.

the number line

Like sets, the term *number line* should be used only informally during the primary years. Although it is more abstract than groupings of beans or pictures of birds, a number line (Figure 14—7, page 132) can help children learn about addition. This model, in common use after the modern math movement was underway, was seldom used before that time except in

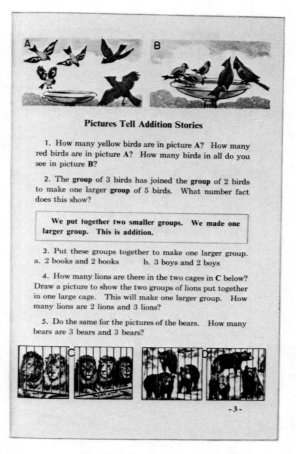

Figure 14–6   Page from Making Number Discoveries *by Leo J. Brueckner, Elda L. Merton and Foster E. Grossnickle (John C. Winston, 1959).*

materials by Catherine Stern. As this approach uses a continuous model of number (length) rather than a discrete one, such as sets and counting do, number lines work for the addition of fractions and negative integers as nicely as for the addition of whole numbers.

Using the number line explanation, 2 + 3 = ____ simply means, "Start at zero, go two units, then go three more units." The units may be counted on an already marked-off line or measured off on an unsegmented line. The answer to "How far did you go?" corresponds to the stopping point.

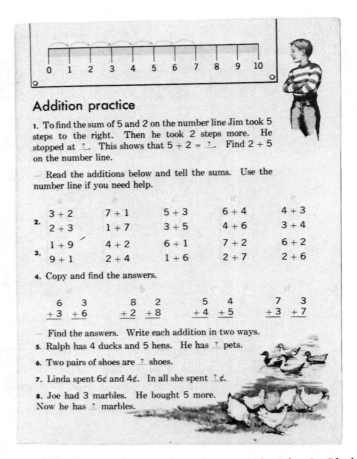

Addition practice

1. To find the sum of 5 and 2 on the number line Jim took 5 steps to the right. Then he took 2 steps more. He stopped at ?. This shows that 5 + 2 = ?. Find 2 + 5 on the number line.

Read the additions below and tell the sums. Use the number line if you need help.

	a	b	c	d	e
2.	3 + 2	7 + 1	5 + 3	6 + 4	4 + 3
	2 + 3	1 + 7	3 + 5	4 + 6	3 + 4
3.	1 + 9	4 + 2	6 + 1	7 + 2	6 + 2
	9 + 1	2 + 4	1 + 6	2 + 7	2 + 6

4. Copy and find the answers.

	a		b		c		d	
	6	3	8	2	5	4	7	3
	+3	+6	+2	+8	+4	+5	+3	+7

Find the answers. Write each addition in two ways.

5. Ralph has 4 ducks and 5 hens. He has ? pets.

6. Two pairs of shoes are ? shoes.

7. Linda spent 6¢ and 4¢. In all she spent ?¢.

8. Joe had 3 marbles. He bought 5 more. Now he has ? marbles.

Figure 14–7 Page from Growth in Arithmetic 3 *by John C. Clark, Harold E. Moser and Charlotte W. Junge (Harcourt, Brace, 1952).*

In using the number lines, tape measures, rulers, or metersticks, many children count spaces rather than points. Children whose answers to addition problems are consistently one number off might be asked to do a sample problem aloud as you watch carefully how the solution is determined.

(Many commercial and teacher-made number lines omit the numeral 0 and begin with the number 1. This practice encourages the belief that zero is not a number and makes later work more difficult. Choose and make number lines with 0 plainly marked on them.)

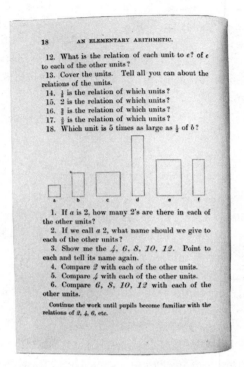

18   AN ELEMENTARY ARITHMETIC.

12. What is the relation of each unit to *e*? of *e* to each of the other units?

13. Cover the units. Tell all you can about the relations of the units.

14. ½ is the relation of which units?

15. 2 is the relation of which units?

16. ⅔ is the relation of which units?

17. ¾ is the relation of which units?

18. Which unit is 5 times as large as ½ of *b*?

1. If *a* is 2, how many 2's are there in each of the other units?

2. If we call *a* 2, what name should we give to each of the other units?

3. Show me the *4, 6, 8, 10, 12.* Point to each and tell its name again.

4. Compare *2* with each of the other units.

5. Compare *4* with each of the other units.

6. Compare *6, 8, 10, 12* with each of the other units.

Continue the work until pupils become familiar with the relations of *2, 4, 6,* etc.

Figure 14–8   Pages from Arithmetics, *by William Speer (Ginn, 1898).*

A concrete analog to the number line is a set of proportional rods. Although some nineteenth century-educators had developed similar materials (Figure 14–8), as had Montessori, those of Cuisenaire are the best known. This manipulative material is especially valuable in presentations to blind children, as the differences in quantity are easily distinguished by touch. Recent research suggests that learning-disabled children and children whose favored style of learning is wholistic rather than analytic also learn better with a measurement approach.

Cuisenaire rods are blocks of wood (or, more recently, plastic) of ten lengths, each with a cross section of one square centimeter. The smallest rod is one centimeter long (and is thus a cubic centimeter) and the largest is ten centimeters long. The colors are standard. The smallest rod is uncolored but is called white. The longest rod is orange. The colors of the remaining rods are, from the shortest: red, light green, purple, yellow, dark green, black, brown, and blue. Color families indicate related numbers—as the "blue-green" family of 3, 6, and 9 or the "hot" colors of 5 and 10.

To introduce addition, a train of two rods is formed and a single rod (or a combination of an orange rod and one other rod) is found that has the same length as the train.

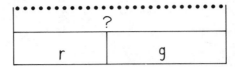

In the strict Cuisenaire program, the rods are designated by color. Thus, in the above example, the addition equation would read

$$r + g = \square$$

The box should be replaced by y, which stands for the five-centimeter-long yellow rod. Many mathematics educators believe the use of color names distracts children or are themselves distracted by statements such as "red plus green equals yellow."

Some proportional rod sets, like the Montessori long stair, are of a single color or of alternating colors. Some have unit markings that may be counted. The Dienes and the Stern materials are of this type. The Cuisenaire approach, however, is solely a measurement approach and has no unit markings.

the balance beam

Although the use of the balance beam as a classroom teaching aid for mathematics was virtually unknown during the first half of this century, it had been used previously (see Figure 14–9). Children enjoy activities with the beam; it is a valuable asset in helping children understand mathematics concepts.

When a beam is in balance, the torque forcing it to rotate in one direction about the pivot point is equal to that forcing it to rotate in the other direction. This balance does not mean that the weights on the two sides of the beam must be equal or that the weights have to be placed at the same distance. What must be the same on both sides is the product: weight × distance. (See the illustration below.) In presenting this device, the teacher might reference balance on a seesaw. Many children have learned from experience that a heavy child must sit close to the center to balance a lighter child.

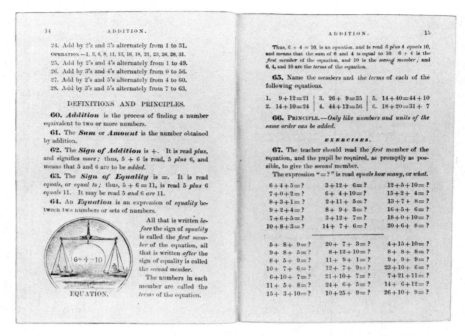

Figure 14–9   *Pages from* Robinson's Shorter Course *by Daniel W. Fish (American Book, 1874).*

Because the two factors operate together to determine the torque, there are two possibilities for the representation of $2 + 3 = $ _____. One

can either keep weight constant and vary distance or keep distance constant and vary weight. Consider a balance with hooks on which weights can be hung.

Distance.   In this case the number of weights is set, and a rule that only one weight can be hung on a hook. The numbers in the addition problem then specify which of the evenly spaced hooks have to be used. $2 + 3 = $ _____ suggests one weight is hung on the 2-hook and one on the 3-hook on the left side. To balance the beam, where must a single weight on the right side be placed? Trial and error will produce the answer "5" in a very short time. Verification of the solution is satisfying and unmistakable.

Weight.   In this case the numbers in 2 + 3 = _____ specify the number of equal weights to be hung on a single hook per side. (A pan balance works the same way.) This approach (Figure 14–9), especially if a pan balance is used, can be varied by varying the items to be weighed (choosing items that are more-or-less consistent in size). Peanuts, acorns, marbles, pennies, or other fairly heavy items are useful. One balance sold as an educational toy by a producer of early childhood educational games uses proportionally weighted numerals. On this device a 5 hung on the hook on one side is actually balanced by a 3 and a 2 or a 4 and a 1 hung on the other hook. (The weighted numerals also make nice tracing materials—see Chapter 9.)

Balances can be purchased or made from pie tins and scrap lumber by those clever with tools. The balance beam has been used only infrequently as a model of whole-number addition and substraction. Those who wish to use math balances, however, will find them inexpensive to purchase or construct and effective when in use. Posterboard models are effective once children have had experience with the "real thing" (Van de Walle and Thompson 1981).

models for subtraction

Each of the approaches suggested for explaning the basic meaning of addition can be used to explain the basic meaning of subtraction. A fifth explanation relies on the inverse relationship between the two operations. There is also a complication that makes subtraction a slightly more challenging concept for children.

Explanations for the subtraction operation can be presented either as a comparison between two separate sets or measured quantities or as the partition of a single one. Although children should eventually learn to recognize both take-away and "how many more?" situations, a formal distinction is of concern primarily to the teacher. Children may be intuitively aware that subtraction situations come in different types, and they should have much opportunity to act them out. No special mention of the difference between take away and comparison situations is necessary, but experience in both cases is vital.

For success in word problems, familiarity with both subtraction modes is necessary. Therefore, teach both modes and by having children make up stories that reflect both and share them orally and in pictures with other

CHAPTER 5

Counting Away

"Let us try something new," said Miss Lee.
"Let us take some away from a group
and find how many are left."

How many books did she put on the table?
How many books did she take away?
How many books were left on the table?
 One from five is how many?
 We say, "One from five is four."

When we take some away from a group
and find how many are left, we are **subtracting**.

54

Figure 14–10   *Page from* Row Peterson Arithmetic Book 2 *by Harry Grove Wheat, Geraldine Kauffman and Harl R. Douglass (Row, Peterson, 1951).*

children. (Artwork or language-experience charts around this operation make a nice display for parents' night.)

counting

Some children instinctively count backwards as a means of solving questions involving subtraction. Although it has sometimes even been forbidden (Thorndike 1921), some texts and teachers suggest this approach to a subtraction problem (Figure 14—10). Counting backwards is also the way answers are found in Chisanbop and Fingermath (Knifong and Burton 1979; Lieberthal, 1979). It is a nice introduction to subtraction (and, later, division).

The sentence $5 - 2 =$ _____ suggests that a person should start at the number 5 and make two counts backwards: "four, three." The last number announced is the answer. A very common error in this approach (I made it myself as a second-grader) is beginning the backward count with the largest number given. In $5 - 2 =$ _____, such children would say "five, four" and give 4 as the answer. As all their answers will be one off, this consistent error is fairly easy to diagnose and remediate.

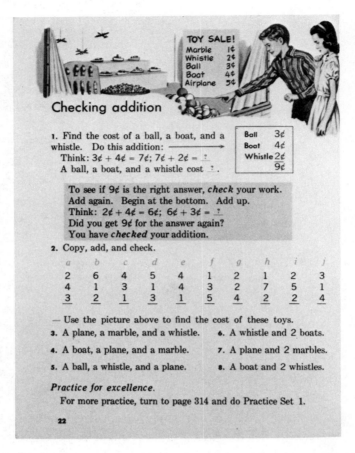

Figure 14–11   Page from Growth in Arithmetic 3 *by John C. Clark, Harold E. Moser and Charlotte W. Junge (Harcourt, Brace, 1962).*

the inverse of addition

From time immemorial children have learned that subtraction "undoes addition" (See Figures 14–11, 14–12, 14–13.) Although this phrase might make a mathematician wince, it does express, in children's language, the important relationship between addition and subtraction. Subtraction as the *inverse of addition* may be a better term for later mathematical studies, but *undoes* is clearer to children (and perhaps to some parents). In this model, 5 − 3 = _____ is explained as another way of writing 5 = 3 + _____. Indeed, many children use addition ("3, 4, 5") to solve 5 − 3 = _____, showing they are confident that addition and substraction "work" this way. Older children find the relationship useful in recalling

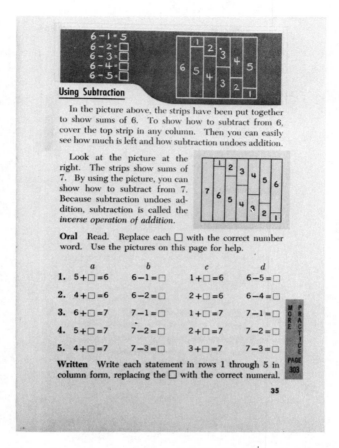

Figure 14–12   Page from Arithmetic 3 by E. T. McSwain, Kenneth E. Brown, Bernard H. Gunddoch and Ralph J. Cooke (Laidlaw, 1965).

number facts. Furthermore, it will provide a reason for (and therefore speeds the learning of) the check most commonly used to verify subtraction problems.

sets

One of the most hallowed explanations for the operation of subtraction is that of sets. In this model the modes of comparison and partition can be more easily distinguished than in either the counting or inverse of addition models. (See Figures 14–14 and 14–15, pages 141 and 142.)

Comparison.   In this mode there are two distinct sets. Nanook has five doggie bones and Lila has three. The comparison question is, "How many

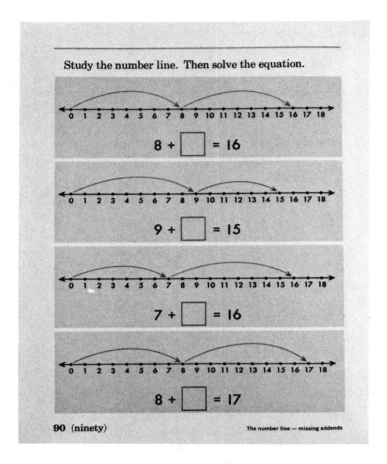

Study the number line. Then solve the equation.

$8 + \boxed{} = 16$

$9 + \boxed{} = 15$

$7 + \boxed{} = 16$

$8 + \boxed{} = 17$

90 (ninety)   The number line — missing addends

Figure 14–13   *Page from* Elementary School Mathematics Book 2 *by Robert Eicholz and Phares G. O'Daffer (Addison-Wesley, 1971).*

more bones does Nanook have?" (or, "How many fewer bones does Lila have?") The answer to this question is often though not necessarily shown by establishing a one-to-one correspondence between the two sets, as in the following illustration. Children can work out this problem with real doggie bones.

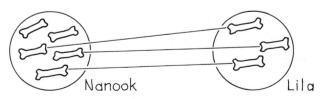

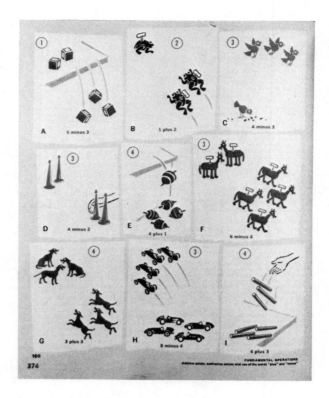

Figure 14–14   *Page from* Seeing Through Arithmetic I *by Maurice L. Hartung, Henry Van Engen, E. Glenadine Gibb, Lois Knowles and Catherine Mahoney (Scott, Foresman, 1964).*

Take-Away.   In this mode 5 − 3 = _____ suggests that in a set of five objects, a subset of three of them is considered. An all-time favorite "take away" example involves five ducks sitting on a pond, three of which decide to fly away. The problem is essentially the same if three of the ducks are black, hungry, male, etc. The questions are how many are left, are a color other than black, are not hungry, are female, etc. In each case there is a group from which some subset is distinguished as being different. A partition situation involving dog bones might be: "Nanook had five doggie bones and three of them were broken. How many were whole?" After the children have acted out the situations they can try to communicate them in shorthand, using numerals and arithmetic signs.

Figure 14–15   Page from Making Number Discoveries *by Leo J. Brueck-ner, Elda L. Merton and Foster E. Grossnickle (John C. Winston, 1959).*

the number line

The number line explanation for subtraction (Figure 14–16) was especially popular in the '60s and '70s. Comparison and partition can be distinguished on the number line models.

Comparison.   In this situation the statement $5 - 3 = $ _____ suggests that Becky's unit hiked five miles from the Girl Scout camp and Dawn's unit hiked three miles along the same trail. The subtraction situation is: "What is the difference in their trips?" or "How much farther must Dawn's unit walk to catch up with Becky's unit?" (See diagram, next page.)

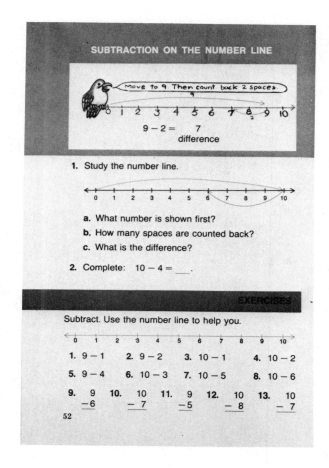

Figure 14–16   *Page from* Holt School Mathematics Grade 3 *by Eugene Nichols and others (Holt, Rinehart and Winston, 1974).*

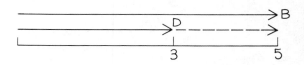

Take-Away.   In this situation the statement $5 - 3 =$ _____ suggests that Becky's group must walk five miles to return to camp. After walking three miles, how much farther will they have to walk?

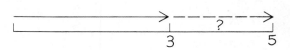

Teachers who wish to avoid later difficulty in translating word problems into equations should be sure students have practice translating real situations of both types into number sentences. At all levels students should be encouraged to make up stories to go with given equations and to match equations with a story another person tells. Simple maps or game boards with (not necessarily straight) paths are especially valuable stimuli for such discussions.

When subtracting on a number line, children sometimes count the "mile posts" rather than the lengths between them. The use of hopping kangaroos, rabbits, and frogs may help children focus on the number of jumps.

Proportional rods are another powerful device for explaning subtraction. Such rods make clear that especially difficult concept, the "missing addend," and are useful with children who need both a visual and a tactical stimulus but think counters are "baby stuff."

Comparison.   If one wished to find $5 - 2 = $ _____ (or $2 + $ _____ $= 5$), a red rod would be placed on top of a yellow rod. The student would then search for a rod that "fit." Only the light green rod will fit.

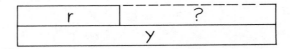

If the red rod is called 2 and the yellow rod is called 5, the light green rod is, of course, 3. It is easy to see, then, that the yellow rod is three units longer than the red rod. Number lines in which the units are spaced one centimeter apart can serve as a bridge from this concrete material to the more abstract number line.

Take-Away.   Although they are clear examples of comparison subtraction, rods make poor models of "taking away" unless some type of shielding device is used to cover the taken-away portion. Such devices may be more combersome than they are worth.

the balance beam

Although the math balance is used less frequently as a method of explaining subtraction than of explaining addition, it deserves mention.

Comparison.   In the case of a hook balance, $5 = 3 + $ _____ suggests that a weight is hung on the left 5-hook and another on the right 3-hook.

The question is: "Where should another "right" weight be hung to balance the beam?" When a pan balance is used, five weights are placed in one pan and three in the other. The blank is to be filled with the number of weights that should be placed with the three weights to balance the scale.

Take-Away.   In the case of a hook balance, $5 - 3 = $ _____ suggests that five washers are hung on the left 1-hook and one washer hung on the right 5-hook. Three washers are removed from the 1-hook. "Where must the single washer on the right side be placed to restore the balance?" The partition mode is clumsier than the comparison mode with this model and is perhaps best avoided with young learners.

the case of 3 − 5

When children meet a number sentence such as $3 - 5 = $ _____, teachers often simply tell them, "You can't do this type of problem." Sometimes a justification like, "If you have only three items, then I can't take five away, can I?" is used. This answer provides poor preparation for later study and need not be resorted to, as even younger children may have met examples of such subtractions. In a board game, for instance, if you advance three spaces and then go back five, you are two spaces behind where you started. It is both mathematically and psychologically correct to tell children that the answer to this problem involves numbers that they will learn about later and that until then they will have no answer to this type of problem.

If a child insists that $3 - 5 = $ _____ is the same as $5 - 3 = $ _____, you might ask the child to try and show both situations using any of the models discussed above. It is always better to allow the child to try to prove a statement rather than to say "You can't do it" or to offer a demeaning "explanation" such as "It's true because I said so." Explanation by teacher fiat encourages the belief that mathematics is capricious and unfathomable—exactly the myth good teachers of mathematics are trying to put to rest.

The benefits of understanding a mathematical topic go beyond simply aiding the development of a particular skill. Explanations that develop true understandings will reference known concepts, understandings, and experiences and will enrich and interrelate them. They will help children incorporate the new concepts into their present views of the world. The

difficulty with which a learner grasps a new idea will be in proportion to
the adequacy of the bridge connecting the new ideas to the old. Children's
ability to solve problems, in turn, depends upon the depth and breadth of
conceptual understanding they bring to the problems. The richer the
concept, the more easily it will be remembered accurately and applied
appropriately. Because examples of most addition and subtraction situations will be met, children should be familiar with all of them. To settle
for less would be to settle for an incomplete explanation of a topic crucial to
the ability to solve problems.

fifteen

geometry

Seminal thinkers of kindergarten curriculum have traditionally valued geometry. Indeed, Pestalozzi formed nearly his entire program on it, and Froebel (Figures 15–1 and 15–2, pages 150 and 151) also gave geometry a central role. Both men used solid as well as plane shapes, and both believed geometric figures were useful in developing sense perception, the basis of all learning. G. Stanley Hall concurred, saying to his early twentieth-century audience that geometry should come early in the school curriculum, almost at the beginning of arithmetic. Contemporary support for the inclusion of geometry comes from those concerned with the school's overemphasis on analytical and verbal skills (Franco and Sperry 1977).

skills at kindergarten entrance

By the time children have reached kindergarten age, they have had a great deal of informal experience with shapes and with the topological concepts of open and closed (see pages   and   of this text). Organized, this experience gives them a foundation for further study. Rea and Reys found that most beginning kindergartners could:

1. Match objects to similar-shaped objects.
2. Match objects to similar-shaped drawings.
3. Match objects to similar shapes on a form board.

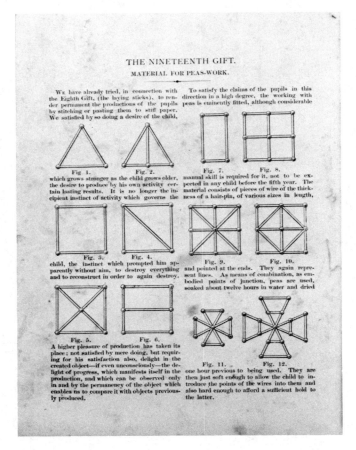

Figure 15–1   *Page from* Paradise of Childhood, *by Edward Wiebe (Milton Bradley, 1896).*

4.   Correctly identify squares and circles.

5.   Correctly identify lines, sides, and corners.

6.   Correctly identify inside and outside areas of geometric shapes.

7.   Make accurate comparisons in terms of length and distance.

8.   Correctly reproduce lines, parallel lines, and perpendicular lines (1971, 401).

A solid basis in geometry is important to the later study of area and perimeter and for the development of visual thinking skills. The primary years are not too early to begin such a study, and the above list of competencies can guide the teacher in designing activities for children.

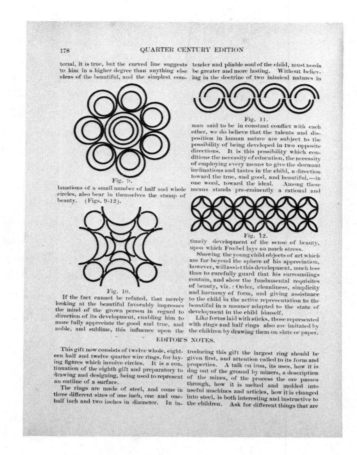

Figure 15–2   Page from The Paradise of Childhood *by Edward Wiebe* (*Milton Bradley, 1896*).

preparing a foundation for later work

Despite the theoretical benefits of early geometry study before the mathematics revolution of the 1960s and early 1970s, geometry was confined to formal study of figures and proofs in the late junior high and high-school years. The inclusion of geometry in the kindergarten curriculum is one of the most enduring of the changes brought about by the "new math." Such inclusion had been argued long before, especially by the Committee of Ten in 1894, but met with little positive reception. Now it is the atypical kindergarten that does not have paper shapes hanging from the ceiling; puzzles in the form of squares, triangles, and circles for the children to make; or bingo games designed to give practice in shape recognition.

From the earliest years geometry study, however informal, should be a definite part of the mathematics curriculum. Proofs, definitely out of place in the elementary curriculum, are certainly even more so at the kindergarten and first- or second-grade level. At those levels, the vocabulary should be simple, and lessons, though thoroughly planned, should be very informal. Instruction need not be confined to the mathematics period. Geometry is appropriate for the art period, when children may use the shapes to create collages and mobiles and when concepts of symmetry may be introduced by folding and cutting exercises. Worksheets or exploration centers might be designed around using geometric figures in designs for greeting cards or quilts; identifying shapes in the environment; finding equal lengths; drawing parallel and intersecting lines; constructing squares, rectangles and triangles on the geoboard; discriminating between open and closed curves; and using geometric words. Egsgard (1969) has developed a structure of the K–12 geometry curriculum in which the importance of early experiences is apparent (Figure 15–3).

During the kindergarten year, children can be helped to develop the awareness of spatial relations prerequisite to the understanding of geometric concepts.

Some signs that children have this awareness is their ability to:

1. Move parts of the body (combined motions of arms and legs, both arms, both legs, cross-lateral movements) upon command.

2. Balance and walk forward and backward on a walking board.

3. Make their bodies use as much space or as little space as they can.

4. Follow an indicated path from one point to another, using chalk and a chalk-board, or a stick or a finger in the sand.

5. Draw vertical and horizontal lines, circles, and diagonals.

6. Place objects "near" others or "far" from them on command.

7. Place items "inside," "outside," "in," and "on" indicated enclosures.

8. Demonstrate with body movements an open and a closed curve.

9. Draw eyes, nose, arms, legs, fingers, etc., in correct order and proximity to each other in a picture of a person.

10. Reproduce with suitable materials one geometric figure enclosed by another.

11. Use concrete materials to show "between," "before," and "after."

12. Replicate the order of a model and reconstruct it in reverse (adapted North Carolina Department of Public Instruction 1977, 4).

Games and activities   Ways to help develop geometric abilities are natural inclusions in the early childhood curriculums. Here are a few of them.

Touch Your Partner

Have children choose partners. Instruct them to touch a part of their partners' bodies a specified number of times. Keep changing the body parts and required number of touches.

Beads

Give each child beads of various shapes and colors. Have children form pairs. Each member of the pair will string ten beads. From oral description alone, the child's partner must duplicate the necklace. (This activity is harder than it sounds.)

Boxes I

Place on the floor large cardboard boxes that have had their tops and bottoms removed. Have children sit on top, go through, look through, hide inside, and go under a given box.

Boxes II

Have the children *pretend* they are inside boxes. Help them explore the edges, corners, and sides of the boxes. Let one child "show" through movement his or her box. Ask the rest to draw what they "see."

Circle Movement

Place large circles on the floor. Have one child stand on each circle. Give directions such as "Jump up and down in your circle" or "Walk around your circle." Doing this to marching music makes it more enjoyable.

Around, Inside, and Outside

Have children stand around a circle drawn on the floor. Then have them walk, jump, or hop outside the circle and then inside the cirle. Again, moving to music of various rhythms enhances this activity.

Listening Game

Draw circles and squares on the floor with tape. Ask the children to stand facing you and obey commands such as "Hop into the square," "Put one foot in the circle," "Trace the square with your foot," and "Put your hand near the circle."

Figure 15–3   *A structure of the K–12 Geometry Curriculum (from Egsgard 1969, 444–445)*

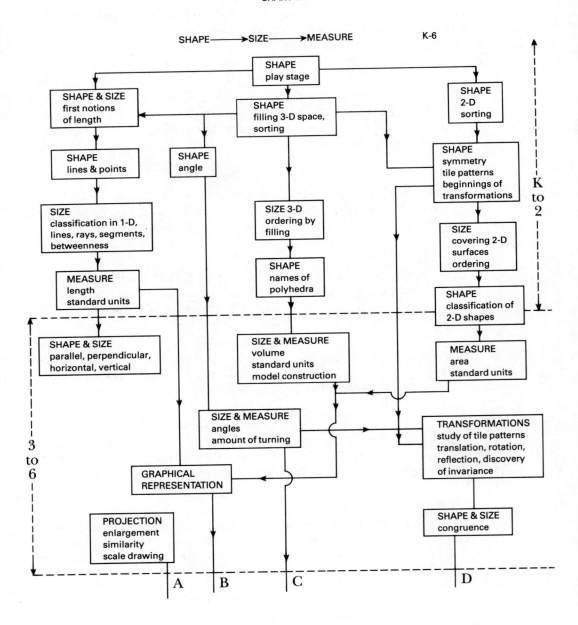

CHART 2

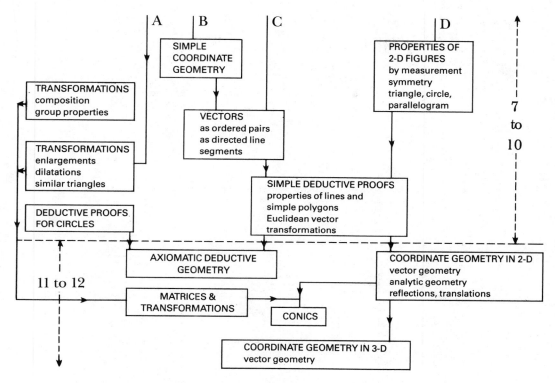

Other activities that give practice in geometric skills are the following.

1. Drawing figures in the air.
2. Constructing figures with pipe cleaners.
3. Tracing figures using a template.
4. Reading books about shapes.
5. Stretching rubber bands on a geoboard to form the shapes.
6. Going on a shape scavenger hunt in the schoolyard.
7. Finding examples of shapes in the classroom.
8. Making torn-paper art based on a single shape or pair of shapes.
9. Identifying three-dimensional shapes by feel alone.
10. Building with wooden block sets containing cones and cylinders as well as cubes and rectangular prisms.
11. Using carpet squares to make a reading area or housekeeping area.
12. Gluing yarn borders onto artwork.
13. Constructing with erector sets, Tinkertoys, or Legos.
14. Making mosaics and patterns with pattern blocks.

15.   Playing "Geometric Bingo" (Figure 15–4). Prepare enough bingo cards for each member of the class, using nine boxes per card. Using circles, squares, rectangles, and triangles, place one shape in each box. Using the colors from their crayon boxes, have the children color the shapes, being sure that each shape of the same kind is in a different color.

Prepare a box full of shapes, with each shape in a different color. Choose one child to "be the teacher" to pick and call out the colored shapes. The first child to cover three in a row wins.

Figure 15–4   *Geometric Bingo*

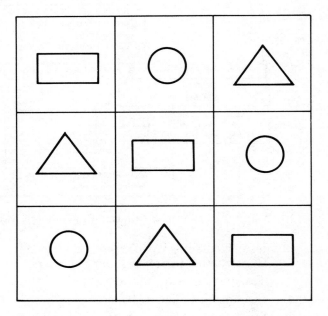

Piaget has shown that children's first concepts of space are topological; that is, concerned with proximity, betweenness, and closure. Even at the earliest stages children have had a great deal of experience with these and other geometric relations, though that experience has not been organized into a cohesive mental structure. Introductory geometry lessons should be designed to provide that structure, which does not mean that children should be required to parrot definitions. Empty verbalization is *never* a valid objective. Helping children build on what is known through active exploration or a prepared environment is the goal for which the wise teacher of mathematics aims.

sixteen

early experiences in measurement

Kindergarten children have had much informal experience with measurement. Many know parts of the day, and seasons of the year. Some have observed parents measuring cloth or wood. Many recall words dealing with time. Most know something about weight, having been weighed themselves during health checkups and having perhaps seen a parent buy fruit or fish by weight. They have an intuitive understanding of unequal volumes having complained often, "He has more soda than me." And they have handled the coins of the realm.

incoming skills

In their 1971 study, Rea and Reys reported (p. 400) that over half of the entering kindergarteners could correctly:

1. Differentiate between the characteristics of size and weight.
2. Identify the use of scales.
3. Identify a clock.
4. Identify the function of a clock.
5. Identify the use of a calendar.
6. Identify a ruler.
7. Identify the function of a ruler.

8. Identify the relationship between height of a column of mercury and temperature (thermometer).
9. Identify pennies, nickels, and dimes.
10. Identify one-, five-, and ten-dollar bills.
11. Order coins and bills according to value (which is worth most, least).
12. Use pennies in a simple problem situation (buying gum).

The approximate timetable for the attainment of measurement concepts has been developed from the research of Piaget by Coxford (1963) and can be seen in Table 2 on page 000 of this text.

what is measurement?

Measurement requires that a child believe in the constancy of the measuring unit under changes of position. Because the majority of kindergarten children cannot yet conserve length, area, mass, volume, weight, and number, measurement understandings are apt to be somewhat shaky. Much can be done, however, as an integral part of the young child's day to provide familiarity with measurement concepts. Some of the basic ideas of measurement that can be stressed at the earliest school level are the following.

1. Measuring is a way of determining "how much" and "how far."
2. Measuring is a way of comparing.
3. Units can be used repeatedly in measuring.
4. Which unit is appropriate depends upon what is being measured.
5. If it takes many small units to measure something, it will take fewer large units.

An excellent way to provide practice in measurement is to establish a measurement center in the classroom. The center, which might be in a corner or on a windowsill, should contain a variety of items to be measured, a variety of items to measure with, nonbreakable containers, a pan balance with raised sides to prevent spilling, and a dustpan and brush. Plastic sheeting on the floor will protect flooring or carpet and will facilitate the removal of spilled material. Some materials you might include in the center are measuring tapes, rulers and metersticks, plastic measuring cups, milk and juice cartons, margerine containers, unit blocks, egg cartons, nails of several sizes, lumber scraps, hammer and saw, nested toys, wooden beads and pegs, pegboards, balls of several sizes, sponges, rocks, paper bags, boxes, scraps of cloth, sets of weights, pan balance scales, timers, clocks, and calendars.

Activities in the measurement center will at first be of the getting-acquainted type but can later be structured by the teacher to include those in which the children:

1.   Make guesses about volume (capacity), weight, length, and distance.
2.   Use nonstandard measuring units to check their guesses.
3.   Select appropriate instruments and units for measuring.
4.   Use scales, stopwatches, trundle wheels, metersticks, cups, and other measuring tools to solve measurement problems.

Extensive experience with measurement will enable children to build up accurate notions of size, shape, and capacity. One of the most basic of these is spatial relations. "We can say spatial ideas do not derive from a 'reading' or direct apprehension of the physical properties of objects, but from an action performed on them (Lovell 1971, 71)." Among the relationships fundamental to measurement that young children must learn are up, down, on, under, over, above, below, before, behind, large, small, far, near, left, and right. It may be hard to realize, but for kindergarten children, sentences combining one or more of these relationships (such as, "The paper is to the left of the bookshelf behind the teacher's desk") are very difficult to decode. Such statements require concrete operational thought, a level of thinking beyond what is possible for the majority of children under age seven.

special problems of the learning-disabled child

Following such directions is especially difficult for the learning-disabled child. Inability to develop spatial concepts may be one of the earliest indications of learning disability (Kaliski 1962). Teachers of young children who notice a child having more than the usual difficulty dealing with the concepts up, down, under, and over (which are among the earliest spatial concepts mastered) might consider requesting formal testing for the child.

Because many measurement concepts depend on spatial concepts, children who have minimal brain damage or who are learning disabled may have a difficult time with measurement activities. Kaliski has suggested that such children may be able to memorize counting and addition facts and thus perform at a normal level in rote number work, but measuring offers no such camouflage. Even such "simple" activities as arranging events in temporal sequence or seriating a set of objects by size may prove extraordinarily difficult for learning-disabled children. Finding the value of a handful of coins may be an impossible task for them, too, even if they seem able to evaluate separate collections of pennies, dimes, and nickels. The practice given such children must be structured, cued to their strengths, and as concrete as possible. The earlier such difficulties are discovered, the less chance there is of frustrating the child. Teachers who give careful attention to children's performance in measurement situations may save some children from continuing failure at mathematical tasks.

measurement activities

Several specific types of measurement are studied in the elementary school years: length, area, volume, weight, temperature, money, and time. Valid activities can be done in all of them at the kindergarten level.

length

Piaget makes a distinction between distance and length; the former is the word used to describe empty space, the latter to describe space occupied by some material. For an understanding of linear measurement, conservation of length is a necessary but not a sufficient condition. Children must also believe that a length can be subdivided without a change in the total length. Such a belief is usually not reached until about age eight.

Children's first experiences with linear measurement should be not with a ruler but with nonstandard units that can be lined up. Some appropriate units are paperclips, new chalk, unsharpened pencils, blocks, pipe cleaners, tongue depressors, toothpicks, and straws. Distances and lengths can also be measured off with hand spans and strides. Linear measurement lends itself to a variety of classroom activities. Measuring beanbag tosses and the growth of plants are two of the most popular. Of course, children like to measure themselves as well.

It is much easier for children to measure an object by lining up several identical objects along it rather than to use one object several times.

Children under age eight are not apt to do the latter with much precision. TWTYS AND Cuisenaire rods make especially good measuring devices because they are readily available and standard in length within each color.

Some children may be ready for more challenging measurement activities. Here are a few you might suggest to them.

1. Find something that is longer than your pencil.
2. Find six things shorter than the blue ribbon. Find six things longer than it.
3. Use your pencil to measure the windowsill.
4. How many toy cars can fit in a driveway made with four green Tinkertoys?
5. Cut a paper strip as long as your shoe.

area

The amount of surface within a closed curve is called the *area*. Young children have little concept of area. Activities like covering surfaces with smaller objects such as paper strips, triangles from a pattern block set, and centimeter cubes are appropriate at the kindergarten level. Some children may be able to trace an object on grid paper and count the squares, but activities involving the concept of area should remain at the exploratory level.

capacity and volume

Piaget makes a distinction between interior volume (or capacity), which is usually conserved by age eight, and true volume (the amount of space occupied by the object), which is usually conserved by age eleven or twelve. Because of these attainment ages, elementary teachers will be most interested in providing experiences leading to an understanding of capacity.

Children enjoy investigating such questions as:

1. How many scoops of beans fill the cereal box? How many scoops of shells fill it?
2. How many cups of water fill the pitcher?
3. How many cups fill the dishpan?
4. How many times can you fill the measuring cup from the milk bottle?
5. Can you find a bottle that holds as much as the green jug?
6. How many tablespoons of water fill the measuring cup?
7. Which holds more water—the red cup or the blue dish?
8. Which holds more rice—the red cup or the blue dish?

All kinds of things can be used as containers: bags, baskets, beakers, bottles, bowls, boxes, cans, cartons, envelopes, jars, margerine tubs, matchboxes, pails, pitchers, shakers, spoons, and plastic bowls. Many materials can be used as fillers: water, salt, cornmeal, fine sand, peas, beans, rice, and Styrofoam chips. Special provision will need to be made for the measuring of water. Ideally a roomy container such as a commercial water table or a baby bath tub should be provided in addition to a sink. It is a good idea to have some large plastic bib aprons on hand as well. The water area should be positioned somewhat distant from the sand table, to discourage mudpie making.

Restrained and structured mixing *should* be encouraged, though. Cooking is a fine way to combine practice in metric and English measuring and important lessons in nutrition. Here are some healthy snacks kindergarten children enjoy making. Only two of these require heating, and for those a hot plate is sufficient.

Peanut Butter Candy

Mix together 2 parts nonfat dry milk, 1 part peanut butter, ½ part honey. Make small balls and roll in confectionary sugar.

Mallow Squares

Mix 3 parts fine graham cracker crumbs, 4 parts tiny marshmallows, 1 part chopped nuts, 1 part sliced dates, 1 part evaporated milk. Roll the mixture in graham cracker crumbs and press into a square pan. Let stand, then cut into squares.

Cookie Filling or Frosting

Mix 2 cups confectionary sugar, 2 tablespoons milk, a dash of salt, ½ teaspoon vanilla. Color, if desired. Spread on vanilla or chocolate wafers.

Gram-ola

Mix well 1 liter oatmeal (uncooked), 5 dl wheat germ, 2 dl shredded coconut, 5 ml cinnamon, 30 ml brown sugar. Mix in 1 dl honey. Add 75ml oil and 5 ml vanilla extract and/or black walnut extract. Add nuts and raisins if desired. Spread in a 25 x 38 cm jelly roll pan. Bake at 325°F for 20 minutes. Store in tightly covered container.

Cereal Peanut Bars

Combine 1 part light corn syrup, ½ as much brown sugar, and a dash of salt in a medium saucepan. Bring to a boil. Stir in 2 parts peanut butter.

Remove from heat, stir in a splash of vanilla, 4 parts crisp rice cereal, 2 parts crushed corn flakes, 2 parts chocolate morsels. Press into buttered pan and let stand.

Choco-Peanut Milk Shake

Blend together 1 tablespoon creamy peanut butter and ¼ cup milk. Place in 2-quart jar with tight-fitting lid. Add approximately 1 quart milk and 3 tablespoons chocolate-flavored drink mix. Cover and shake well.

Maply Syrup

Mix in a pan 6 dl confectionary sugar, dash of salt, and 2 dl water. Bring to a rolling boil and boil 1 minute. Remove from heat and add 10 ml molasses and 5 ml maple flavoring. Serve on pancakes, waffles, & French toast.

Apricot Coconut Balls

Chop 1¼ cups dried, uncooked apricots. Add 2 cups shredded coconut; blend in ⅓ cup sweetened condensed milk. Shape mixture into small balls and roll in confectionary sugar.

Other snacks children enjoy making are biscuits from a biscuit mix, instant pudding, and punch from a powdered mix. Such experiences give the children a chance to feel capable and enjoy the fruits of their labor as well as to learn the uses of measurement. (Recipes can be converted from English to metric units using the table in Appendix I.)

weight (mass)

Rea and Reys (1971) found that 75 percent of their entering kindergarten children knew the difference between size and weight. Experiences in ordering by weight and using standard weights will still be needed, however, by most children. Commercial materials are available for the ordering exercises. Montessori, for example, suggested using rectangular pieces of wood of the same size that varied by weight. The Baric tablets, as they are called, can be purchased from a supplier of Montessori equipment. You might also make your own set for weight ordering by filling identical boxes or cans with substances varying in weight such as popped popcorn, sand, Styrofoam chips, large lima beans, and rice, and then sealing the containers so none of the "filling" can escape.

Children usually enjoy weighing things. Such experience should first be of the form "Which is heavier—two nails or three bottle caps?" A balance with a pan on each side is the best type of scale to use. Many are available with raised sides to help contain the objects being weighed. Children might use cards like these

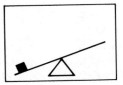 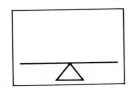 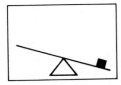

to show which object was heavier. Almost any material can be used in these activities: bottle tops, spools, bobbins, shells, stones, horse chestnuts, dried peas, beans, rice, macaroni, screws, nuts and bolts, old keys, heavy and light parcels, buttons, and nails, to name a few. Teacher-made activity cards will serve to get the children started, but the children will soon pose and solve their own problems.

While the word *weight* has been used consistently in this section, the teacher should be aware that what we have been talking about is technically called *mass*. The weight of a body is the force with which gravity pulls on it; weight varies with the body's location. Mass is the amount of material in a body, and it is constant. Very few children below the age of eight will be able to conserve weight or mass.

Children will form a clearer understanding of weight if they try to lift various objects. They might even pantomime carrying an object and have others guess if it is heavy or light. Teachers, too, can join in the dramatics.

temperature

Children at the primary level will be most interested in temperature as it affects their lives. "Put a sweater on—it's too cool for just your shirt." "Have a cold drink—it's so warm today." "Don't touch—hot!" "My, your cheeks are cold!" "Have you got a fever? Your forehead is so hot!"

Montessori suggested that bottles filled with water of varying temperatures would be good seriation items. This activity is apt to be a bit unwieldly for most classrooms, though. Perhaps the best that can be done on the topic of temperature is a discussion of the outside and inside temperature each day and a discussion of seasonal variations, where they exist. (It has always annoyed me that discussions of winter in early childhood curriculums betray an assumption that winter always means snow and ice. The only ice children in the South see is on TV or in their freezers; neither is correlated with the seasons.) Making predictions for tomorrow's weather is a nice way to end each day.

money

Many first graders can identify coins and dollar bills. Some have had experience paying for objects and receiving change or gifts of money. For young children, however, counting a handful of coins is an extremely difficult task. For most it is meaningless as well, because the numbers involved are beyond those they comprehend.

The U.S. monetary system is complicated—much more complicated than the system we use in counting. In our monetary system we group sometimes by twos, sometimes by tens, and sometimes by fives or fours. In the decimal system we group only by tens, and *that*, as any teacher will attest, causes *enough* problems.

A multitude of experiences in counting and exchanging real coins will help children develop an awareness of the value of these deceptive pieces of metal. The author can offer no explanation of the reasoning behind the sizes of the coins; she can only warn you that convincing a young child that a dime is worth more than a nickel is hard work. The following poem by Shel Silverstein contains more truth than fiction.

Smart

My dad gave me one dollar bill
'Cause I'm his smartest son,
And I swapped it for two shiny quarters
For two is more than one!

And then I took the quarters
And traded them to Lou
For three dimes—I guess he don't know
That three is more than two!

Just then, along came old blind Bates
And just 'cause he can't see
He gave me four nickels for my three dimes
And four is more than three!

I took the nickels to Hiram Coombs
Down at the seed-feed store,
And the fool gave me five pennies for them,
And five is more than four!

And then I went and showed my dad,
And he got red in the cheeks
And closed his eyes and shook his head—
Too proud of me to speak!

(Silverstein 1971, 35)

As in all of mathematics, the three different classes of learning—facts, skills, and concepts—must be considered when it comes to teaching children about money. There are pieces of verbal information (a nickel is worth five pennies) without which it is impossible to function in a system, culturally accepted responses to monetary situations (a given amount can be arrived at by various combinations of coins), and psychomotor processes (making change). Facts can be taught in rote fashion; concepts require understanding and therefore must be taught differently; skills require manual and cognitive facility. All these types of knowledge must be in place before an individual is prepared to solve the problems that will be presented explicitly and implicitly, verbally and in print, throughout her or his lifetime.

To teach facts, it is suggested by most mathematics educators that children be cognizant of the interrelations among the facts. As human beings, we seem to be able to remember connected items better than isolated bits of information. Perhaps you can recall having to memorize the capitals of the countries of the world or the states of the U.S. These were unconnected facts. Knowing the capital of Rhode Island is Providence was no help in naming the capital of Maine, even though the states are quite close geographically. Learning the Roman numerals, however, is an example of a network of information. Knowing the pattern for writing the equivalents of 1, 2, 3, and 4 in Roman numerals makes it easier to learn to write 10, 20, 30, and 40. Helping children form these networks will aid retention and lessen the time needed for reteaching.

Concepts, you will remember, must be taught using a variety of instances that vary in all but the essential features. The activity of finding coins that total fifty cents should be presented with as many variations as can be managed. As in most concept teaching, it is wise to start with the real objects and then move to pictures before asking the children to attempt work at the symbolic level, which means that initial instruction in this area should begin with real coins (not play money) and proceed through play money to pictures of money to verbal presentations.

Skills call for a large quantity of corrected practice if they are to be used effortlessly. When making change, it is best to start with the purchase of a single item close in value to the tendered amount. Once a child can make change when there are few options you can present more complicated situations. Making change is a complex learning situation and should be delayed until children can discriminate among coins, add and subtract one- or two-digit numbers of the type found in the activity, and find equivalent coins for any given amount up to the amount required. Taken together, this means that the time-honored procedure for teaching about money, the classroom store, is not appropriate at the introductory level. Most children are not ready for it until at least late first grade. Remember that repetitious practice can be boring even to the motivated student, so do try to use a variety of activities when developing skills.

Monetary equivalences present a heavy memory load and require a good deal of cognitive flexibility. These demands can make learning about money a real challenge to mentally retarded students or to learning-disabled students troubled with preservation or perceptual problems. Practice in a variety of interesting situations will be necessary, with special attention given to the particular difficulty experienced. The child who has difficulty with size perception, say, can perhaps be taught to notice verbal or pictorial clues on coins and bills. If the child has trouble even then, perhaps his or her kinesthetic sense is fine tuned enough so that the coins can be discriminated by weight. Regardless of age, students who are nonconservers may be loathe to admit that a pile of coins has the same value as a single silver-colored piece. Reviewing the events of instruction (Appendix F) will help you devise appropriate lessons in this difficult but essential topic. You will have to be creative and adapt instruction to each individual's strengths and weaknesses, but, after all, that is what the teaching is all about.

Problem solving using money often occurs in the real world where there are no pencils and paper props. If students are to achieve proficiency in solving these problems, they must eventually be able to operate under real-world conditions, even though they should not begin their study of money problems at that level. Those who have traveled to a foreign country where they are unfamiliar with the monetary system can attest to the frustration of trying to remember the value of the currency, choose that which adds to or exceeds a purchase, and check the change received. It is not unusual for tourists to give up the struggle, proffer a handful of coins and bills, and trust the seller to take only enough to cover the purchase. Avoidance is one way of coping with cognitive tension—in this case it is probably not the best way. You can help children escape that state of high anxiety by carefully controlling the pace of instruction and the level of difficulty of the problems presented. Building a solid foundation for later learning is especially important in the area of money.

The ability to solve problems involving money is one of the most important goals of the mathematics curriculum. No one who lives in the real world can afford to rely solely on the kindness of strangers. When decisions have to be made about which areas of the curriculum to stress and which to omit, let money be one of the former.

time

Teaching about time is also amazingly complex. Rea and Reys (1971) found that less than 25 percent of their sample of entering kindergarteners knew the day of the week, month of the year, or date of their birthdays. Although 50 percent knew what a calendar was used for, few could read it. Although all knew what a clock was, only a few children could tell time on one. Some children could recite the days of the week, but few could recite the months of the year.

Gesell, Ilg, and Ames (1946) suggest that by the age of four a child can tell morning from afternoon and by age five can tell what day it is. By age seven a child can tell time, but it is not until the age of eight that a child knows the month, season, and year. The notion of time is not only important in its own right but also must be understood if the notion of speed is to be understood.

Time is a very difficult concept and demands careful teaching in the early school years. Relating time to the daily life of the children, such as naptime and lunchtime, is very helpful. Personal time is understood by some children as early as five or six, but it is not until some four or five years later that a sense of historical time is developed (Lovell 1971). As you will note, this is long after children have learned to "tell time"; that is, to read time from a clock face. Understanding the concept of time is built on understanding the concepts of duration and sequence, the vocabulary of time words, and the concept of equal intervals.

The unit by which we measure time, the minute, cannot be seen and handled like the centimeter or the gram. Watching events that terminate or timing the duration of an action can help children form an idea of the length of a minute. (However, even adults know that time seems to expand and contract on a situational basis. An hour in the arms of your sweetheart and an hour in the dentist's chair certainly appear different in length.) Children might observe dripping water to see how long it takes to fill a small container, use a stopwatch to see how many blocks a friend can stack in a minute, or count the swing of a pendulum as a minute passes. Games of "beat the timer" are fun. Guessing how long it will take an ice cube to melt gives children a sense of longer periods of time.

Helping students appreciate the concept of measurement may take longer and may require more creativity than using the "it's true because I said so and I'm the teacher" technique. Whenever concepts are to be learned and completely understood, however, explanations and experience are more desirable than commands. Only when they understand will students be sure of the mathematic ihpin measurement situations and will they enjoy using their skills in situations that make sense to them.

seventeen

a special activity:
graphing

Graphing is a way of recording collected data. It can be used to find answers to questions, can act as a nonverbal description of a situation, can arouse the creative abilities in children, and presents a natural opportunity for vocabulary development. Graphing gives children a chance to extend their classification skills and to use numbers in interesting ways; it will be encountered through the child's mathematical studies, so it deserves a place in the early childhood mathematics program.

The sequence that provides success in graphing is the same sequence that provide success in other mathematical activities: use real objects, then pictures, then abstract symbols; begin simply, and then move to more complex situations. Recommended graphing experiences at the kindergarten level are the following.

1. Using real objects.

    a.   Considering only two conditions.
        Examples: Have children separate glue jars into those that are full and those that need filling and then line them up accordingly.

             Have children separate crayon boxes into those that contain some broken crayons and those that do not. Have them put those with broken ones in one line and the rest into another.

b.   Considering three conditions.

Examples: "Which is your favorite kind of cookie in this box—vanilla, chocolate, or oatmeal?" Let each child put one cookie in a bag and place it in the appropriately labeled column.

Ask children to line up near the science corner, the art table, or the free-reading area. Discuss the length of each line.

c.   Considering four conditions.

Examples: Have children with only brothers line up in one line, children with only sisters in another line, children with both brothers and sisters in another line, and only children in a fourth line.

Using four different designs of holiday paper plates, have children choose their favorite and construct a bar graph with the plates.

2.   Using pictures of objects.

a.   Considering only two conditions.

Example: Give each child the same size piece of paper and ask them to draw a picture of themselves. Put the pictures of boys in one column and the pictures of girls in another.

b.   Considering three conditions.

Example: Make copies of each child's school picture. Using these small pictures of the children, have each child place his or her picture in the column showing a picture of an ice-cream cone with his or her favorite ice-cream flavor. Offer three flavors for choice.

c.   Considering four conditions.

Example: Give each child a piece of paper of the same size. Have each child write his or her name on it and draw an answer to the question, "What is your favorite season?" Place the slip in the appropriate column according to the picture drawn.

3.   Using Symbols.

a.   Considering only two conditions.

Example: Let the children taste a new food. Have those who like it take a red checker and those who don't like it a black checker. Make a stack of each color.

b.   Considering three conditions.

Example: Make available three colors of Unifix cubes. Tell the children to take a red cube if they'd prefer apple juice for snack time that day, an orange cube it they'd prefer orange juice, and a white cube if they'd prefer milk. Make vertical towers with each set of chosen cubes.

c. Considering four conditions.
    Examples: Give each child a paperclip or a link from a Lots-a-Links set. Label four columns *cat*, *dog*, *fish*, and *bird*. Ask the children to attach their links to the label naming the pet they would most like to have.

All graphs constructed should be thoroughly discussed so that children become comfortable with the interpretation of recorded data.

Graphing need never be dull. By changing the topic graphed and the indicator of count, graphing can be an exciting part of your daily schedule. Objects that can be used for real graphing include books, pencils, jars, children's shoes, spools, hats, wrapped candies, crackers, toy animals, cookies, glasses of juice, and fruits. Some questions that might be asked to form the graph include "Which color do you like best?", "Which is your favorite?", and "Which will you choose for snack today?"

Useful at the pictorial graphing level are pictures drawn by the children, pictures of the children, children's name tags, and illustrations cut from magazines. At the symbolic level, counters need not look like the depicted item. Materials such as checkers, Unifix cubes, rings to fit over dowels, linking objects such as Lots-a-Links or paperclips, colored squares of paper, clip-on clothespins, or pressure-sensitive dots can be used. Data gathered might include favorite TV shows or snacks, number of missing teeth, color of eyes and votes for books to be read during storytime. Once the graph is constructed, mathematical questions can be generated at first by the teacher and later by students. Questions such as "Which color was the favorite?", "How many more people chose graham crackers than chose saltines?" and "Which juice was least often picked?" will begin discussion on the graphed data.

During graphing activities, make sure that each "vote" receives equal weight. In this way information can be reliably obtained from the height of the column (or length of the bar) as well as from counting votes. The easiest way to do this is to provide a surface ruled off into square sections. If the graph is to be constructed with real objects, a long piece of plastic (such as is used to protect carpets) that has been sectioned off by strips of masking tape works well. If you prefer to use heavy paper, it can be ruled off with permanent markers. Baratta-Lorton (1976) suggests that each child be supplied with a personal graphing box made from cut-off half-gallon milk cartons that bear the child's name or picture. Items can be placed in the box for graphs with real objects; the empty boxes themselves will generate the graphs on the pictorial level. Sections taped together will hold smaller items or pictures.

To illustrate the flexibility of the mathematical topic of graphing, here are some detailed suggestions. Remember that talking about what one has done is a powerful aid to understanding it. Encourage *much* conversation.

1. A birthday graph. Mark twelve columns on a large sheet of paper. Divide each column into sections. Label each column with a month of the year. Let each child color one section of the column labeled with the month in which he or she was born. When all the birthdays have been recorded, ask questions such as:

> In which month are there the most birthdays?
> In which month(s) are there no birthdays for this group?
> In which months are there few birthdays?
> Are there any months that have the same number of birthdays?
> How many children have a birthday when school is out for the summer?

2. Color and compare. Give each child a piece of grid paper two squares high and ten squares long. Color some of the squares in each row. Ask all the children whose first colored row is longer to place their pieces of paper in a row. Those with a second row longer will put theirs in a second row. Those papers with both rows the same length will make up the third row. Questions around the complete configuration are easily generated:

> How many people colored more squares in the first row?
> How many colored more in the second?
> Did more people have a longer first row than had a longer second row?

3. Picture graphs. Have each child draw a flower and color it red or yellow. Ask those who have colored the flower red to place the picture in one column and those who have colored it yellow to place it in a second column. Now ask some questions:

> How many children colored their flowers yellow?
> How many red?
> Of which kind were there more?
> How many more?

Have each child take back the picture and draw a cat or dog on it. Ask questions as before.

Do other graphs based on adding details to the drawings. Be sure to spend time discussing the results of each graphing activity.

As you display the pictures in the hallway or on the bulletin board, ask the children to describe them using the characteristics by which they were classified.

4.   Estimation activities. A most important mathematical skill is estimation. Children can begin to develop this skill in kindergarten. With teacher guidance guessing games such as "How many beans are in the cup?" and "How many people do you think will choose chocolate milk today?" will help children begin to develop estimation strategies.

Put out a bowlful of peanuts in the shell. Ask children to guess how many peanuts they will be able to hold in one hand. Ask them to pick some up and count the peanuts. Repeat the experiment several times.

The data from this activity can be used to make graphs for each child. As the activities are repeated, the children can then use the graphs to make "better guesses."

Don't let the fact that *you* never saw a graph until sixth grade prevent you from including graphing as a regular part of your kindergarten mathematics program. It is an interesting, socially useful, and mathematically sound topic and is well worth any trouble you go to in order to supplement the program suggested by the teacher's manual or the district guidelines.

eighteen

teaching the number facts: no frustration necessary

Many adults cite learning "the tables" as one of the most frustrating tasks of the elementary school years. Tear-stained pages and upsetting classroom episodes revolving around the learning of the 100 basic addition facts are not uncommon. (The author had to learn 144 addition facts—in the "old days" people learned the 11 and 12 tables, too—so she has felt the pressure first hand.) Yet teachers and parents alike agree that it is important for children to know their tables. Can children be helped to acquire this skill with less emotional upset? Yes, I believe they can. And how grand it would be if each child left the second grade knowing all 100 addition facts at the immediate recall level and left the third grade with the 100 multiplication facts well memorized! These learnings are well within the power of almost every child.

Memorizing the facts as important as learning the computational process such as 34 + 17 or 46 − 19 will not be exacerbated by uncertain recall of the facts. Here are some guidelines for teachers as they help children towards mastery of the tables: (1) Make the task clear, (2) use prior learnings and mathematical properties, (3) plan the work in easy steps, and (4) use a valid testing procedure (Knifong and Burton 1982).

Memorizing or knowing at the immediate recall level means being able to give an automatic, correct reponse. Some children can give these answers using other means, however (Brownell and Chazal 1935). Many children (and adults) who "know their facts" do not have them memorized but use developed skills in rapid counting or indirect recall. Many adults do the latter. They memorize a few facts and use those facts to figure out the rest. For example, $7 + 6 = \underline{\hspace{1cm}}$ becomes $6 + 6 = 12$, followed by $12 + 1 = 13$; or perhaps $7 + 3 = 10$, followed by $10 + 3 = 13$. Thus, if memorization is the goal, it is essential to make that goal clear. Memorizing the basic facts is an example of learning at the verbal information level, and the rule of thumb for this type of objective can guide teachers who wish to motivate children to succeed at this task. Helping children note the usefulness of ready recall of the number facts, providing evidence of progress, offering verbal and nonverbal rewards for success, and providing opportunities for spaced practice are among the rules of thumb.

Anyone would be disheartened at the prospect of memorizing 100 isolated bits of information for automatic random recall. (How would you feel if you were asked to memorize the days of the week on which November 26 falls for the next 100 years?) But there are features of addition that help reduce the task. The first has to do with our hero, zero. If a student has learned the concept that any number added with zero is just that number, the child does not have to *memorize* the "zero" facts. Secondly, the child who realizes that any number added with one is just counting one more does not have to memorize each of the "+1" facts. And finally, the child who is aware that the order of the addends does not matter has only half the table to worry about. Such whittling leaves 36 addition facts to memorize (Figure 18–1), which is still a big job, but 36 *is* less than 100.

The goal of ready recall can be reached in an effective and humane manner if the effort is spread over most of the school year. The second-grade teacher can begin by reviewing the properties mentioned in the previous paragraph. The real key to easing the burden, however, is to assign only *one new fact per week* to be memorized, beginning with $2 + 2 = 4$ and testing the children individually in face-to-face interviews (Knifong and Burton 1982). Any student can work ahead, but those who know the week's facts can be assured that they are right on schedule. For many students this will be a unique experience, and one to savor. Keeping a record of memorized facts will document the child's progress.

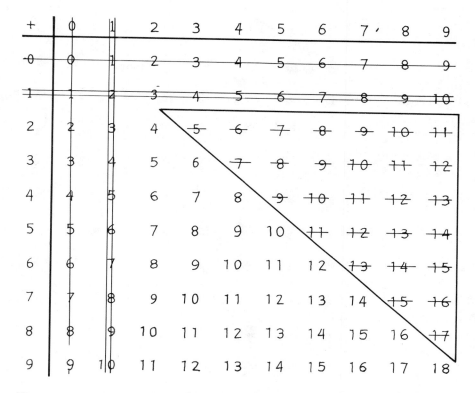

Figure 18–1   *Addition Facts that Must Be Learned*

How can "second-grade work" be done if students must spend the year memorizing facts? Easily. As you teach the algorithms, allow each student to use his or her individual addition fact chart on which gummed labels or colored magic marker circles have been used to cover the memorized facts. A large version of the addition chart in Figure 18–2 (page 178) might be displayed on a bulletin board for a class studying 5 + 5 = _____. A child who has learned all the number facts assigned and who has such a chart available to check the *unlearned* facts will be able to concentrate on understanding the algorithm. The very act of checking will correct wrong responses and reward correct ones, thus speeding up the memorization task.

To facilitate the learning of the fact of the week, teachers may wish to provide practice in class. It is helpful to recall that short drill sessions are much more effective in helping a child commit facts to memory than are a

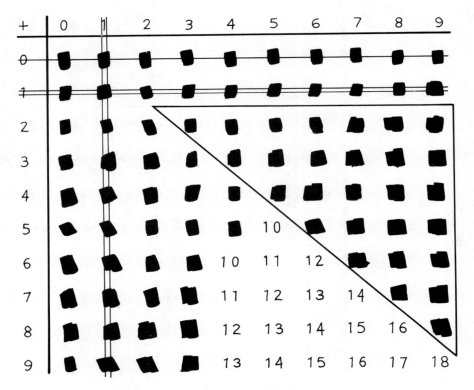

Figure 18-2   A Number-Fact Chart for Reference

few lengthy, widely spaced sessions and that accuracy is more important than speed at first. Five concentrated minutes are enough, if they occur about three times a week. This is not the time to explain what addition means; that explanation should have come before. The student's whole attention should be on giving the correct answer to the posed question. It is a sound practice to request that the student say the whole fact and not just the answer. Repeating the sentence "four plus five equals nine" will help the answer come more easily to mind next time "four plus five equals what?" is asked. For less intense drill, board or card games that provide practice on the number facts are also very valuable and easy to construct (Ashlock 1981).

When parents ask if there is anything they can do to help their child learn the facts, the teacher might suggest that two or three minutes a day could be spent on the task. Parents can set a timer for two minutes or estimate a job that takes about that long and ask the facts that have already been learned, including every so often the fact of the week, until the time is up or the table is cleared. This activity helps in what is considered by parent and teacher alike an important aspect of elementary-school mathematics and will generate a bond between those who desire the child to succeed. Working together on this aspect of the child's program can facilitate feelings of competence in the parent, professionalism in the teacher, and success in the child. Everyone wins!

The two basic methods of testing children for automatic recall of number facts are timed paper-and-pencil tests and individual interviews. Unfortunately the first of these, though quick to administer and grade, is not a valid test for immediate recall. A child who has memorized some of the 100 items can respond quickly to these and will have time to count or use indirect recall to find the others. In addition, timed tests are a prime antecedent of anxiety and as such are best avoided. They also train and reward fast counters.

Asking each child face to face for the fact of the week in such a way that one knows if the answer was given immediately or mentally worked out is a more valid test of direct recall. Requesting that each child initiate the fact-of-the-week interview encourages the assumption of responsibility for task accomplishment as it simultaneously eases the task of the teacher (Knifong and Burton, 1982).

Remember that it is important to ascertain that the fact is automatically recalled. A student who introduces irrelevant words may be buying time to apply an indirect method. To avoid testing for short-term memory only, the teacher can ask several previously studied facts before presenting the test item. Such a procedure both provides a review and prevents the child from employing the type of temporary recall adults use while they move to dial a phone number they have just looked up. Ideally the conversation should be private so the teacher can reward children for successful tries and correct children for unsuccessful ones without witnesses.

Record keeping is not difficult. Keeping a poster such as is shown in Figure 18–2 up to date can be a class helper task. A class roster with learned facts checked off under each pupil's name can be maintained by the teacher in the grade book.

Learning the number facts *can* be a rewarding experience in mathematical power and personal confidence. There is no need to perpetuate feelings of incompetence in this area. Too many adults count under the table or blanch at the sight of a restaurant check to be divided. By providing children with both the tools to learn these all-important facts and access to the facts that they have not yet learned, teachers will give children the freedom to attend to learning the numeral-processing skills that will play such an important role in the application of mathematics in daily life.

nineteen

teaching place value

Place value is often cited as the most difficult topic to teach in the early elementary grades. It seems plausible and is often asserted that most cultures developed a base-10 numeration system because human beings are endowed with ten fingers. Some cultures (notably the Mayan—a hot-climate culture in which people went barefoot) had a base-20 system. Some use another grouping principle.

When children get addition examples such as 42 − 47 incorrect, it is often wrong to say "This kid just doesn't know the number facts!" Even 100 percent accuracy with respect to the number facts and knowledge of what subtraction means in the face of an incomplete or faulty understanding of place value, can lead to discouraging performance on two-digit problems. Sadly, all too many students have a less-than-adequate understanding of place value.

When you teach place value you are more apt to be successful if you apply these basic strategies for good mathematics instruction.

1. Begin by using concrete objects.
2. Provide material to each student.
3. Use many different aids.
4. Consider language as you instruct.
5. Allow the student time to think when he or she is asked a question.
6. Do not hurry on to the next unit too rapidly.

In addition to these general directions, one specific to place value can be added: Begin with appropriate materials.

types of materials

Although a wide variety of aids have been used by teachers to introduce place-value concepts, all the aids fall into just two categories: proportional and nonproportional. In proportional aids, the object standing for 10 is ten times as long, wide, heavy, thick, or numerous as the object standing for 1. You can *see* the difference between a bundle of ten sticks and a single stick, for example. Nonproportional aids depend upon some attribute such as color or position to show the distinction. Dimes and pennies are nonproportional aids. Within the proportional aids, two types may be distinguished: collectibles and exchangeables. All nonproportional aids are of the exchange variety. Single collectible aids are grouped in some visible way until the base number is reached. They should be then bound or joined together in some way so the groups are identifiable. Exchangeables are used differently. Ten single objects are traded or exchanged for one object representing ten units.

Because the bundling directly engages the learner in an activity that mirrors the mathematics, instruction in place value should begin with proportional collectible aids. Once children begin to understand the concept, exchangeable aids are useful and less cumbersome to manage. Plan to spend a long time with proportional aids; do not move too quickly to nonproportional aids. Be even more cautious about moving to pictures or symbols; make this move only *after* the concept is thoroughly understood at the concrete level. Even then, worksheets should accompany the collectible or exchangeable material so the child can work out the problems with materials as the symbolic recording is made. Be sure to work in both directions—from symbols to grouped materials and from grouped materials to symbols.

Collectible Proportional Materials

Type A	Type B
beans, nuts, nails, buttons, shells, popcorn kernels, plastic bread wrapper closures, macaroni, pebbles, cereal shapes	strips of card stock, Popsicle sticks, pipe cleaners, plastic straws, coffee stirs, toothpicks

Collect By

1. Counting them into muffin cups or margarine tubs	1. Placing the item in orange juice cans or half-pint milk cartons
2. Placing them in a plastic bag, which is then securely closed	2. Securing a stack of ten with a rubber band or pipe cleaner
3. Putting them one per section into an egg carton that has had the two end sections removed	3. Sticking the items into a ball of modeling clay or Playdough
4. Counting them into plastic pill bottles with snap-on caps	

Once children can count to ten and recognize the ten items as a group, they are ready to begin using proportional collecting devices. Although the look of the apparatus can and should vary, the concept that ten ones equal one ten and one ten equals ten ones remains the same. Abstracting *conceptual* similarities in the *perceptual* differences is not an easy task. Be patient. Here is a list of some aids that have been used successfully by other teachers.

10 beans exchanged for a Popsicle stick with 10 beans glued on it.
10 white Cuisenaire rods exchanged for 1 orange rod
10 single interlocking cubes exchanged for 1 stack of 10 cubes
10 single beads exchanged for 1 string of 10 beads
10 centimeter squares exchanged for 1 10-centimeter strip

Young children and children with mental and perceptual handicaps may have difficulty remembering when to stop and form a group. Structured material such as the Stern counting board or number track or the teacher-made ten-frames suggested by Wirtz (Figure 19–1) are especially

Figure 19–1   *Stern Place-Value Materials and Wirtz Ten-Frame with Beans*

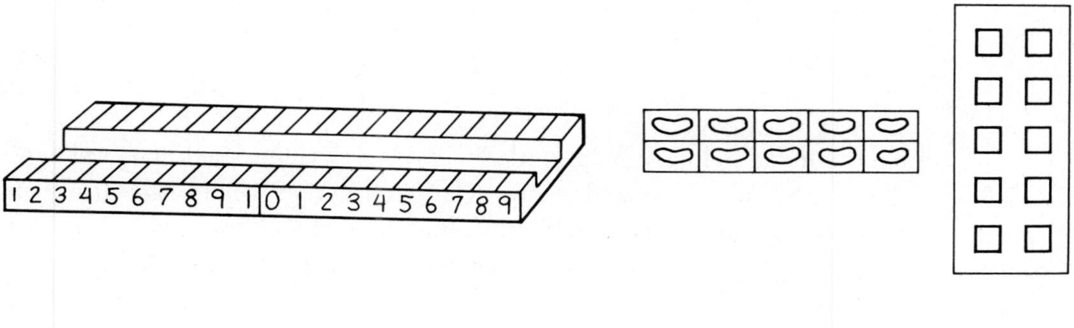

helpful in helping students "notice" 10. To make the Wirtz frame, cut wire fencing into pieces having two rows of five holes each to serve as collectors for beans or other small counters. (Dipping the cut ends of the frame into glue will assure that the children won't get scratched). Asking children to count aloud as you beat a drum or clap your hands and accenting the 10 with a louder clap or a drumbeat will also help children "notice" 10.

Nonproportional aids work on the exchange principle, but the device that signifies 10 is *not* ten times as large as the object used for 1, therefore, they are more abstract than proportional devices and add to the memory load for children.

10 pennies exchanged for 1 dime
10 red chips exchanged for 1 yellow chip
10 green stamps exchanged for 1 blue stamp
10 red triangles exchanged for 1 red square
1 counter on the right-most stick of an abacus exchanged for 1 counter on the stick to its immediate left
1 paper strip in a section of a place-value chart exchanged for 1 paper strip in another section of the chart
10 Is exchanged for one X (as in Roman numerals)

Many sources (Ashlock 1981, Baratta-Lorton 1976, Schminke and Dumas 1981, Schokoohi 1978) are available for help in planning lessons that encourage the development of sound place-value knowledge. That knowledge is crucial to students' mathematical progress whether they are progressing at a normal rate in a "regular" classroom, in a special class for the mentally retarded, or assigned for special help in a resource lab.

using place-value devices in remediation

One of the most common errors encountered by teachers is this one:

$$\begin{array}{r} 42 \\ -27 \\ \hline 25 \end{array}$$

How can you help a student with this problem? He or she seems to know the number facts and understand what subtraction means. The focus of remediation must be on helping the child develop a mature understanding of place value. As you work, remember to keep constant the order of written numerals and their representation. Units should always be on the extreme right, followed by tens (and later hundreds and thousands, in that sequence).

collectible materials

The process that will be similar for all collectible materials is illustrated with cubes. Ask the child to count out four sets of ten cubes and snap them into ten stacks. Then ask that two single cubes be put on a colored mat beside them. Record on a sheet the number of cubes counted out.

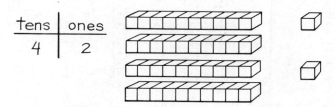

Subtraction can be done in two modes, "take away" and "compare." Because most children understand the take-away mode intuitively, it is an appropriate choice for initial instruction. Ask a child to give you seven single cubes. You will probably receive some response like "I've only got two, so I can't give you seven." Suggest to the child that a tens stack might be broken into units and those put into the single blocks; when this is done, be sure the record sheet is modified.

tens	ones		tens	ones		tens	ones
4	2		³ 4̶	¹2		³ 4̶	¹2
− 2	7		−2	7		−2	7
						1	5

Now the child can easily give you seven ones and two tens. Be sure the complete procedure is recorded. In initial instruction, checking by restoring the two groups of ten and five ones with that of two tens and seven ones to see if they still make forty-two is a good idea. Be aware that when you ask a child to check you are effectively doubling the assignment—use sound judgment in how many examples the child can be expected to complete within a reasonable amount of time. Some learning-disabled children need many changes of activity within what seems to most adults a very short time span. Do not require children who are proficient at the task to do many additional examples—this breeds boredom and frustration.

exchangeable proportional materials

To relieve the monotony yet still provide copious practice, you can vary the type of material used. For example, consider the problem in the previous paragraph done with paper strips. Laminate a grid of a convenient size, and then cut the graph paper into one-inch square pieces and ten-inch strips. For easier handling, a larger grid can be used. Punch a hole in each small piece and ten holes in the ten-centimeter strip. The material is now ready to be used on an overhead projector or on a desktop.

When exchangeable proportional materials are used, the 10 must be traded in for ten units. In this case, one strip must be exchanged for ten small squares. A similar procedure used with beansticks (Figure 20–2). Beansticks are proportional aids made from dry beans and craft (or Popsicle) sticks. To make a ten-stick, glue ten beans onto a craft stick with white glue, and then cover the entire stick with glue so the beans will be securely fastened. The glue will dry clear and the stick will be practically indestructible. The children can make the sticks during initial place-value instruction. Hundred-rafts can later be made by gluing ten ten-sticks to a pair of parallel craft sticks.

If you have access to Cuisenaire rods, you can incorporate these into remedial instruction in the same way. The white and orange rods from the Cuisenaire rod sets will provide proportional aids that are especially handy during the reteaching of algorithms. Ten white rods, each one cubic centimeter long, are equivalent to one orange rod, one decimeter long. Either colored card stock or painted dowels cut in those lengths can be used in place of the Cuisenaire material.

Montessori encouraged the use of both proportional and nonproportional aids. The proportional aids she sanctioned are the golden beads: single beads, strips of 10, and arrays of 100 beads. Inexpensive substitutes can be made with room divider beads. Available in ropes of fifty feet, these plastic spheres come in many bright colors. The fifty-foot length can be cut at any point, even into single beads.

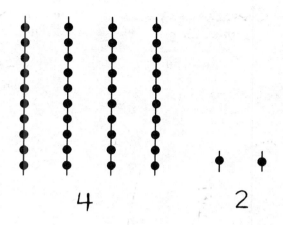

These bead lengths are proportional aids of the exchange type. A string of beads must be traded in for ten single beads before the subtraction of twenty-seven can be accomplished. No scissors are allowed.

nonproportional materials

In conjunction with her proportional aid, Montessori also suggested the use of a nonproportional aid—colored stamps. A green stamp represents 1, a blue stamp 10, and a red stamp 100. These colors (repeated in the next period for 1,000; 10,000; and 100,000) correspond to the colors on the Montessori abacus, another nonproportional device.

As older children may find proportional materials babyish, it is good to have a large repertoire of nonproportional devices ready. Here are a few you might consider.

1. The milk cartonholder.
Cut two holes the size of six-ounce juice cans in one side of a one-quart milk carton. Place one juice can in each hole, and you have an instant collector especially useful for straws or stirs. (The juice cans are not absolutely necessary but give stability to the device.)

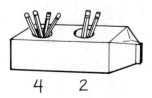

2.   The flipper or odometer
     Divide an 8½″ x 11″ piece of tagboard in half with a vertical line.
Number two sets of ten small pieces of tagboard from 0 to 9. Punch two
holes in the small numbered cards and two corresponding holes on each
side of the large card. Attach one set to each side of the large card using
two metal rings on each side. You now have a counting board. Cards can be
flipped backwards as children subtract.

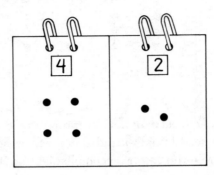

An odometer made from a paper towel roll that has been segmented
can be similarly used.

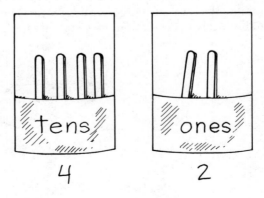

An old standby for teaching place value is the pocket chart. Inexpensive pocket charts can be made from denim, corduroy, or upholstery
material or from card stock. Popsicle sticks or card stock strips serve well
as markers.

Counting people are an adaptation of the pocket chart.

Another nonproportional place-value device, chip-trading activities, assign the values 1, 10, and 100 to various colored chips. Davidson (1974) has developed a comprehensive program of chip trading. If the purchase of this material is beyond your financial limit, you might consider buying the guide books and supplying your own chips. The standard poker chips do not match the colors in the program, but counting disks or bingo markers can be purchased in many colors, as can pressure-sensitive dots.

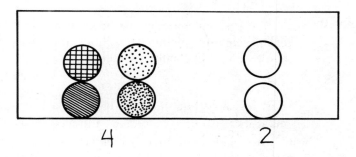

Sound place-value knowledge as well as immediate recall of the basic facts are important prerequisites for learning the computation algorithms. Because you want to be a teacher who believes "the place to improve the world is first in one's own heart and head and hands, and then work outward from there" (Pirsig 1975, 291), you will want to know how to remediate children's conceptual errors, make the materials that will help them in this task, and care enough to spend the time with them as they set about the task.

twenty

developing skill with the addition and subtraction algorithms

"We do not contemne rewles, but we gladly teach rewles; and teach them more plainlie, sensiblie, and orderlie than they be commonlie taught in common scholes."

Robert Recorde (1515–1568)

It is desirable but not strictly necessary to understand how an algorithm works in order to process numerals correctly. There is no one "best" way to add or subtract two- and three-digit numbers. Although some algorithms (or rules) have been used more widely than others in the United States, other algorithms have been popular in other times and places, and some have been recently developed for special students.

There is general agreement that an approach based on understanding is preferable to one based on obedience and memorization. Yet such an approach has in the past even been argued against in the professional literature:

A good computer works as automatically as possible so far as his actual computation is concerned. If he is efficient, each step in the computation is reduced to the plane of habit and he proceeds from one step to the next with as small an expenditure of thinking or reasoning as possible (Upton 1935, 251).

> No explanation is necessary beyond showing the pupils that (an algorithm) works . . . Teaching him to use numbers is much like teaching him to start and stop a trolley car; he may soon learn the trick, but he will not know why it works nor need he know, for his purposes; it is number craft he wants (Wolford 1924, 401).

However, from the same NCTM yearbook that contains the Upton article we read a statement more consistent with present-day opinion:

> The child who merely puts down 2 and carries 1, as a dog does a trick, who borrows merely according to rule, who inverts the divisor because the teacher says so, who places the decimal point in multiplication in unquestioning compliance with a device in the book, will not, in the long run, be so good a computer as the child to whom these acts have meaning (Buckingham 1935, 52).

Many adults are living proof that algorithms learned as rote "follow-the-steps-and-don't-ask-questions" routines can be competently executed. The effects of such learning are often felt when such operations must be applied in novel situations. Those who do not understand the algorithms often develop idiosyncratic techniques for deciding which rule to follow. This is humorously illustrated by Stevenson's (1925) report of a young girl who was usually very good at solving problems but who sometimes chose an unjustifiable algorithm. Here was her method:

> "If there are lots of numbers I adds. If there are only two numbers with lots of parts (digits) I subtracts. But if there are just two numbers and one littler than the other, it is hard. I divides if they come out even, but if they don't I multiplies (p. 102)."

Other research (Bradford 1925) showed that, given impossible problems such as

1. A boy is five years old and his father is 35 years old. If his uncle is 40 years, how old will his cousin be?
2. If Henry VIII had six wives, how many had Henry II?

over half the children worked out answers. Because problem solving is *the* major goal of mathematics instruction, it would seem advisable to assist children in understanding the "why" as well as the "how" of the algorithms.

alternative algorithms

It is easy to assume that the algorithms we learned as children are the only ways that can be used to process numerals. To illustrate that the methods in common use today are not the only ones that work, a few algorithms popular in the past and two new low-stress algorithms follow.

addition

Addition, the most commonly employed of the algorithms, is also the one least changed since the Hindu-Arabic numerals came into general use. Unlike division or even multiplication, addition is a fairly straightforward process. In the first printed arithmetic (a work by an unknown author and published in Treviso, Italy, in 1478), rules for addition of multi-placed numbers are set forth that are very familiar to students and teachers today.

"Therefore, if we wish to add 38 and 59, we write the numbers like this:

$$59$$
$$38$$
$$\text{Sum} \quad 97$$

We then say, '8 and 9 make i7[1] writing 7 in the column which was added, and carrying the i (for when there are two figures in one place we always write the one of the lower order and carry the other to the next higher place). This i we now add to 3, making 4, and this to the 5, making 9, which is written in the column from which it is derived. The two together make 97 (Smith 1959, 5–6)."

This same method had also appeared in a handwritten text published early in the thirteenth century, *The Crafte of Numbrynge*. Two methods of checking the correctness of the sum, subtracting one number from the sum and casting out nines, were suggested in the Treviso arithmetic. We use these same proofs today.

A second algorithm, this one used by Hindu Bhaskara in 1150, was to add the units, record the sum, add the tens, record the sum, add the hundreds, record the sum, and then add partial sums together. The difference between this and the Treviso method was that in the second

---

[1]The use of *i* for the numeral 1 was a common practice during the Renaissance.

case the first additions were done horizontally. A similar method adapted to vertical notation was given by Gemma Frisuis in 1540:

$$
\begin{array}{r}
9279 \\
389 \\
\underline{479} \\
27 \\
22 \\
9 \\
\underline{9} \\
10147
\end{array}
$$

It was usual to place the addends in order of size, with the largest on top, probably to assist those unfamiliar with these "foreign" numerals to keep the columns straight (Jackson 1906). Many people use a similar process in mental arithmetic.

Another sixteenth-century variation, preferred in Europe until the early nineteenth century, worked in a reverse order from left to right, as children who teach themselves may do:

$$
\begin{array}{r}
9279 \\
389 \\
\underline{479} \\
9 \\
9 \\
22 \\
\underline{27} \\
10147
\end{array}
$$

When dustboards were used, the partial sums were often rubbed out, leaving only the answer.

Leslie (1817) reported that addition with deficient figures was easier because it avoided carrying. Here is an example. Do you agree? (The deficient figures are underlined.)

$$
\begin{array}{rrr}
9279 & 93\underline{21} & 10200 \\
389 & 4\underline{11} & \underline{-53} \\
\underline{479} & \underline{5\underline{21}} & 10147 \\
 & 102\underline{53} &
\end{array}
$$

Working in base 12 was another "helpful" algorithm suggested by Leslie.

A recently developed algorithm (Hutchings 1976) illustrates the continuing search for useful methods of dealing with large numbers:

Example		Example		Example	
			3		$1\ 3$
9	9_1	45	$4_7\,5$	286	$23_181\ 6$
7	17_6	96	196_16_1	437	$4_7\ 34_17_3$
5	15_1	37	$39\ 7_8$	519	$15_2\ 15_19_2$
6	6_7	83	187_13_1	806	$18_0\ 0_5\ 6_8$
4	14_1	59	152_19_0	444	$44\ 49_14_2$
	31		32 0		24 9 2

Can you see how it works? Hints: (1) Only the units digit is added, and (2) each column is treated like a units column. Hutchings developed this procedure, which he calls a low-stress algorithm, for use with children who are mentally retarded or who have memory deficits.

subtraction

Subtraction usually causes little difficulty as long as the number to be subtracted is smaller than the "top" number. When it is larger, special strategies have to be used, and they often cause children who try to learn them by rote much difficulty.

You can experience how confusing this approach can be if you try to follow this complementation procedure for subtraction where the subtrahend was greater than the minuend found in the Treviso arithmetic of 1478. Given

$$
\begin{array}{r}
452 \\
-348 \\
\hline
\end{array}
$$

the author writes:

> We cannot take 8 from 2, but 2 is the complement of 8 with respect to 10, and this we add to the other 2 which is above the 8, thus: 2 and 2 make 4, which we write beneath the 8 for the remainder. There is, however, this condition, that to the figure following the 8 (viz., to 4) we add 1, making it 5. Then 5 from 5, which is an equal, leaves 0, which 0 we write beneath.
>
> Then 3 from 4, which is a less from a greater, is 1, which 1 we write under the 3, so that the remainder is 104 (Smith 1959, 8).

The work is checked by addition and by casting out nines or sevens. The complementary method was known to both Bhaskara and the author of

Crafte of Numbrynge and has been rediscovered by children in recent times (Davies 1978).

Morton in 1938 listed five subtraction algorithms that were in current use: take-away with borrowing (or decomposition), take-away with carrying (also called equal additions), addition with borrowing, addition with carrying, and the use of complements. All had been proven since the sixteenth century (Jackson 1906). The additive forms, also called the Austrian Method in Germany and the Italian Method in England, were the focus of much dispute among American mathematics educators during the nineteenth and early twentieth centuries. Consider the example:

$$\begin{array}{r} 524 \\ -78 \end{array}$$

To use the additive (or making-change) method, one would say:

"What can I add to 8 to get 14? "What can I add to 7 to get 11?"

In "borrowing," the second step would look like this:

$$\begin{array}{r} {}^{1} \\ 5\ 2^{1}4 \\ -\ 7\ 8 \\ \hline 6 \end{array}$$

In "equal additions," the second step would look like this:

$$\begin{array}{r} 5\quad 2\ ^{1}4 \\ -\ ^{8}7\quad 8 \end{array}$$

Although all the algorithms have had strong advocates, the take-away with borrowing has been a popular conceptualization of subtraction since the twelfth century. It was the plan easiest to use on sand tables and is incorporated into the new low-stress algorithm subtraction designed by Hutchings (1976):

$$\begin{array}{cc} \begin{array}{r} 5\ 2\ 4 \\ -\ 7\ 8 \\ \hline \end{array} & \begin{array}{r} 5\ 2\ 4 \\ 4\ {}^{1}1\ {}^{1}4 \\ -\ 7\ 8 \\ \hline \end{array} \end{array}$$

explaining contemporary
whole-number algorithms

As is clear by now, many procedures "work." Whereas one algorithm might be handier or less clumsy than another, any algorithm that yields a correct answer should be acceptable. As Warren Colburn wrote in 1830:

> Nothing is more discouraging to scholars than to interrupt them when they are proceeding by a method which they perfectly comprehend, and which they know to be right; and to endeavor to force them into one which they do not understand, and which is not agreeable to their way of thinking. And nothing gives scholars so much confidence in their own powers and stimulate them so much to use their own efforts as to allow them to pursue their own methods and to encourage them in them (Colburn 1970, 34).

Memorizing number facts and becoming skillful with an algorithm is valuable so that sums, differences, and later products and quotients can be efficiently determined. Decisions about which operation to apply to a given situation and how to interpret the results of the algorithm come from an understanding of the operator and not from an understanding of how the algorithm works. As history and personal experience amply demonstrates, many of the approaches were strictly mechanical in nature. Just because this has been so does not mean these approaches do not provide the best course to follow. We *can* learn from the past.

Mathematics educators today believe it is best to develop skill with an algorithm through an initial explanation. Most explanations involve written notation; some mimic the algorithmic procedures through the use of manipulative materials. Although the operations of addition and subtraction are discussed in pairs, each is, of course, usually taught separately.

using manipulative materials

The proper initial approach to teaching the addition and subtraction algorithms uses physical materials other than pencil and paper. Although not the final ways to find sums and differences, these algorithms properly precede the pencil-and-paper process. To a person with a firm understanding of a pencil-and-paper algorithm, counting out objects to find a sum can be downright boring and distracting; therefore, these approaches are quite easily discarded once a child is capable of using numerical notation alone. The time at which this happens, like the length of incubation for all concepts, varies greatly from individual to individual.

loose objects

One of the simplest materials used to illustrate addition or subtraction is a collection of small objects such as pebbles, beans, sticks, cubes, or shells. A fundamental obstacle to the use of any such material is the bother of counting out the necessary number of objects. Unlike marks in the tally system, though, real materials can be grouped to facilitate this counting out. The list of collectibles in Chapter 19 will give you some ideas of what objects can be used.

pocket charts

A strategy almost as popular as bundling sticks is placing these sticks in pockets. These may be pockets on a file folder or card stock base or pockets made with heavy cloth. The pocket chart is easier to use if it is made to hang from hooks or to stand independently.

In beginning work with pocket charts, bundles of ten are placed in the tens column; in more advanced work a single stack stands for a bundle of ten sticks (Figure 20–1). (Be sure children realize that one stick in the ones column represents one, but one stick in the tens column represents ten.) A typical teaching sequence is using bundles until the children are familiar with the tens grouping and switching to representing the bundles with a single stick (sometimes color coded) as the children become annoyed with the cumbersomeness of grouping materials.

Figure 20–1   Using a Pocket Chart

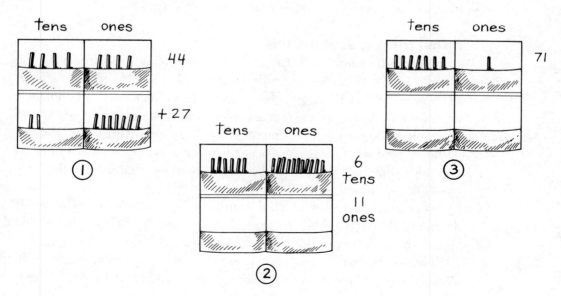

counting or tens people

Similar to the pocket chart approach in which one stick in the tens positions represents a bundle of ten sticks, the counting or tens people material assigns values to the fingers of various cardboard figures. The hands may have magnets that hold metallic fingers or places for fingers like clip-on clothespins. Exercises can be completed either using a single sum of each value of tiers or arranging the people so that the fingers are passed from one to another. If this material is to be used, it might be a good idea to first act out the algorithm using children from the classroom.

the abacus

Any mathematics materials catalog for an abacus contains many of these devices. They are also easy to make (Burton and Knifong 1982). There are only two major types of abacus, one of which is more suitable for the teaching of the basic algorithms. In order to be most appropriate for helping children understand the algorithms for addition and subtraction, an abacus must mirror the base-10 system. Although one can compute sums with any abacus, some (principally those designed along the lines of the Chinese and Japanese abacus) do not mimic the base-10 procedure but substitute one of their own. Such devices will tend to confuse the child who must later adapt to a different process. (Chisanbop, which mimics the Korean and Roman abacus, should be avoided for the same reason.) The abacus can present problems in manipulation for young children and is therefore most useful in upper-grade remedial situations.

flats, longs, and cubes

Currently many well-designed structural materials are available. Usually a square or cubic unit is designated as 1, a line of them as 10, a flat of them as 100, and a large cube as 1000. These materials can double as units for length, area, and volume exploration. Sometimes they are scored to encourage counting and sometimes not (as Cuisenaire rods). Experts disagree about whether the absence of marks makes it more or less difficult for children to understand that the longs represent ten units and the large blocks one thousand units.

A related material of which the author is especially fond was originally developed by Wirtz (1974). In this schema, beans represent 1, beansticks 10, and beanstick rafts 100. A stack of 10 beanstick rafts makes a cube of 1000 beans. Beansticks are a handy size for use with a place-value chart. When the chart is made from a standard 8½" x 11" sheet of paper, there is

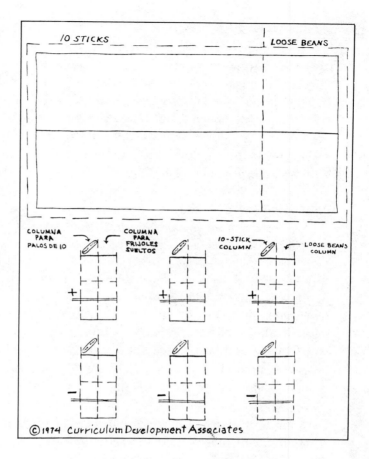

Figure 20–2.   Page from Drill and Practice at the Problem-Solving Level
(*Wirtz, 1974, 110B*).

still plenty of room to write the problem and collect the beans on the same
piece of paper. Thus arithmetic is clearly a record of real-world events, or,
as Wirtz declared, "Mathematics is a record of what we do with stuff." If
loose beans were previously used to illustrate the meaning of the addition
operator, the teacher can introduce the addition algorithm as a simple
extension of the meaning of the basic operation; that is, addition is really
only putting some beans in one rectangular area, recording how many are
there, and then putting some in another area, recording how many are
there, and finally recording how many beans there are altogether in both
areas. Subtraction is shown by taking some beans away from a collection
(Figure 20–2).

using pencil and paper

learning rules by rote

Learning rules by rote is a simple, direct, and widely used approach. Indeed, it is the method that would be chosen by most lay people asked to teach the addition algorithm. It is also the one many of us as well as our parents and grandparents learned. Unfortunately it will not help a child develop an understanding of the addition algorithm. Used in the earliest arithmetics in England, *The Craft of Numbrynge* (ca. 1220) and *The Art of Numbrynge* (1488), this approach consists of listing steps in the procedure, illustrating the procedure with an example or two, and then providing copious exercises for (usually unsupervised) practice.

The acquisition of any chain of behavior depends on the acquisition of each individual behavior, the degree to which a child has learned the correct order of steps, and the amount of correction a child receives during practice. Assuring such learning calls for energy, time, and concern on the part of the teacher. A child who practices errors is in worse shape, mathematically speaking, than one who has not learned the algorithm at all. Vigilance to ensure that the child is following a valid procedure is necessary. Providing such corrected practice was an appealing promise of programmed learning and computer-assisted instruction (CAI); for the most part, monitoring practice is a human endeavor. A major problem with the rote method arises from the need for learning the rules themselves. When rules are detailed and precise, the learner loses the thread of the argument; when they are vague, the learner may have little structure to underpin the new learning. For most children, general but clear instructions work best if the rote learning approach is used.

Whereas the child who is taught by a rote method may have trouble remembering the rules, an even more serious problem is associated with this method. A child who is offered no explanation for the procedures and is told only to do a set of steps until he or she "knows" them perfectly comes to view mathematics as an arbitrary set of rules. When the reason offered for the fact that the rules work is that they give the right answer, children are not motivated to think about the "why" of the mathematics. Such a task fosters neither creative thinkers nor confident users of mathematics. In addition, to forget a single step is to be left with no recourse other than to give up.

Children consistently discouraged from thinking about the process that leads to the answer are not apt to think about their answers any more than teachers asked to memorize a list of nonsense syllables will attempt to try to decode them for spelling rules. Because alertness to the reasonableness of answers, estimation, and problem solving are all important goals for school mathematics, it might be better to use one of the following approaches that attempts to aid this understanding of processes rather than the "do-it-this-way" method.

expanded horizontal notation

A popular new-math algorithm for addition and subtraction used a proof format. In it, each step was justified in terms of the number properties. This style of algorithm, which assumed children were able to do logical deductive proofs, has fallen into disuse at the elementary level.

expanded vertical notation

Although expanded vertical notation is similar to the just-presented horizontal notation, it corresponds more closely to the actual steps of the standard algorithm most children will be asked to adopt as the final form.

Addition

$$
\begin{array}{cccc}
47 & 40+7 & 40+7 & 40+2 & 40+2 \\
+25 & 20+5 & 20+5 & 30+9 & 30+9 \\
& & 60+12 & 60+10+2 & 70+2 \quad 72
\end{array}
$$

$$
\begin{array}{cccc}
& & & 10 & 10 \\
47 & 40+7 & 40+7 & 40+7 & 40+7 \\
+25 & 20+5 & 20+5 & 20+5 & 20+5 \\
& & 12 & 2 & 70+2 \quad 72
\end{array}
$$

Subtraction

$$
\begin{array}{cc}
72 & 70+2 \\
-25 & +(20+5)
\end{array}
$$

The necessary use of parentheses can be confusing to children. To get around the parenthesis problem, some teachers replace + with *and* but this format is probably best avoided at the primary level.

$$
\begin{array}{cccc}
72 & 70 \text{ and } 2 & 60 \text{ and } 10 \text{ and } 2 & 60 \text{ and } 12 \\
25 & 20 \text{ and } 5 & -(20 \text{ and } 5) & -(20 \text{ and } 5) \\
& & & 40 \text{ and } 7 \quad 47
\end{array}
$$

A somewhat briefer form of the expanded notation uses columns labeled to remind children of the symbols' meanings.

Addition

	tens	ones		tens	ones		tens	ones
47	4	7		^{1}4	7		^{1}4	7
+ 25	+ 2	5	+	2	5	+	2	5
					2		7	2

Subtraction

	tens	ones		tens	ones		tens	ones
72	7	2		^{6}7	12		^{6}7	12
− 25	− 2	5	−	2	5	−	2	5
							4	7

Columns have the added advantage of helping the student bedeviled by a poor memory or by poorly developed left-right discrimination skills.

partial sums

The partial-sums approach is a popular initial teaching of algorithms; it is useful for the addition algorithm. A compensation method of historical interest but seldom taught today is used in the parallel format for subtraction. (Many people, however, use this process when subtracting "in their heads.")

Addition

47	47	47	47
+25	+25	+25	+25
	12	12	12
		60	60
			72

Subtraction

72	72	72	72
−25	−25	−25	−25
	−3	−3	−3
		50	50
			47

The partial sums approach can be combined with place-value columns to make the algorithm less demanding of the child. The blend is a good first choice for the child who has difficulty learning mathematics. Only after these intial algorithms are mastered should the standard algorithm be presented as a shorter, quicker way to proceed. Indeed, teachers of children who have difficulty with arithmetic might consider the partial sums algorithm as an appropriate final goal of instruction.

a note on subtraction

The method most used in subtraction in contemporary America is called the decomposition method. It is shown in the just-presented examples; however, it is not the only possible choice. The equal additions method has also had a wide following:

$$
\begin{array}{r}
7\,^1 2 \\
-\,\cancel{2}\,^3 5 \\
\hline
4\ \ 7
\end{array}
$$

In this algorithm, ten is added twice, as one ten in the tens place in the lower number (the subtrahend) and as ten ones in the top number (the minuend). Thus the value of the total problem is unchanged.

A second alternative to the decomposition method also involves equal additions and is used by many of us when we have to work without pencil and paper:

$$
\begin{array}{r}
77\ \cdot \\
\cancel{72} \\
30 \\
-\cancel{25} \\
\hline
47
\end{array}
$$

These approaches are as correct as the one you are most familiar with, and a child comfortable using them should not be asked to switch.

mechanical aids to calculation

Throughout the history of mathematics education, various devices have been constructed to alleviate the tedium of long calculations. The most widespread of these has been the abacus, a counting frame or configuration on a dust-covered table. (The name *abacus* comes from the word *dust*.) In some places the abacus served simply as a record of a computation made in the head; in others it was itself used to derive an answer. The three primitive types of devices were a sand or dust-covered board written on with a stylus, tablets or tables with lines drawn on them for use with loose counters, and tables or boxes with grooves for loose counters. Later, computations were done on beads attached to rows according to the pattern established in the area. Other counting devices were the bamboo counting rods used in Korea; wax tablets that were popular in Rome; and the slate, known from Chaucer's time and replaced by paper only a few decades ago. Although rapid reckoning has always been valued, during Shakespeare's time the abacus was held in low esteem, and a derogatory term for shopkeepers was "counter casters." The modern descendants of the ancient counters are still used in poker games and to keep score in billiards. Tally sticks, knotted cords, finger reckoning—all these have been used by people to help compute and record large numbers.

Mechanical forerunners of the modern electronic pocket calculators were in existence over 300 years ago. They were slow, clumsy, and limited in their uses. Even in 1908, however, they were in demand and were expected to make an impact on schools:

> Characteristic of our time is the extensive use of arithmetical machines (such as adding machines and instruments from which per cents may be read) and of tables (of square roots for certain scientific work, interest tables for banks, etc.). The initial invention of such appliances is not recent—it is their variety, adaptability, and rapidly extending usefulness that may be classed as a present phenomenon.
>
> They have not, however, eliminated the necessity for training good reckoners. They may have narrowed the field somewhat, but in that remaining part which is both practical and necessary they have set the standard of attainment higher. Indeed, an important feature of the present situation is the insistent demand of business men that the schools turn out better computers. There must soon come in school a stronger emphasis on accuracy and rapidity in the four fundamental operations (White 1908, 56).

That arithmetical machines were expected to be a positive rather than a negative influence on learning can be seen from an impassioned statement of a mathematics educator of the time:

> The individual is thus freed and so increases his power of production. Those who deprecate this suggestion might as well deprecate the use of sewing machines, and their introduction into girls' schools. In neither the one case nor the other is there a loss of independence; on the contrary, there is a gain (Carson 1913, 67).

Most modern mathematics educators, the author included, would take a similar stand with respect to the pocket calculator. For children with memory deficits, the intelligent use of a calculator may be as necessary— and just as acceptable—as eyeglasses are to many of us who have visual deficits.

developing skills

A thorough understanding of one or more of the previous explanations will not guarantee that a child will be a proficient calculator. The number facts must also be known well, but even this is not sufficient. Unless that understanding is tested with a variety of practice exercises, the child will not be truly competent with the algorithm. If the goal is consistent accuracy in situations where computing the answer is required, corrected practice is a necessity.

The current need to perform these algorithms has diminished considerably since the turn of the century, when children were expected to be quick and accurate at adding problems such as:

$$\begin{array}{r} 6798657 \\ 3285494 \\ 3847629 \\ +1265835 \\ \hline \end{array}$$

At that time adding machines and calculators were rare, and business had a great need for employees who could calculate rapidly and well. Today when accurate calculations are required, a small electronic calculator is usually used. A number of random but necessary calculations still present themselves in daily life when a machine is not available; thus, it is important that children learn to process numerals.

In an effort to assure this learning, teachers sometimes become concerned over the proper language to use in instruction. Many of us first refer to the process of adding a tens digit of the first column sum to the next column as "carrying." Whether it is permissible to say "I carried the one" is a frequent worry. Proponents of the modern math movement generally frown on this term. Although it has been in use for centuries, and although it accurately described the action of the early reckoners who actually *did* carry a counter from the ones column of their line abacus to the tens column, "carry" does not name a mathematics procedure. The replacement term suggested is *regrouping*. As this term accurately describes the process by which 47 (4 tens and 7 ones) is thought of as 3 tens and 17 ones, it should be used whenever possible. "Borrowing," like "carrying," is also best replaced by the term *regrouping*.

"Is it all right to write down the carried figure?" is another frequent question. Some teachers scorn "crutches" and expect children to remember the number to be regrouped and added to the next column or not to cross out the regrouped number in subtraction. Others want children to write the number at the top of the next column in addition, perhaps even circling it to highlight it, and carefully crossing out in subtraction. As you make your decision about this matter, remember that children will probably make fewer errors (and you can locate those they make more easily) if "crutches" are encouraged, at least at first, to record the regrouped digits. My own opinion is that children having difficulty in learning mathematics should be encouraged to lean on a crutch. Those who do *not* need crutches should be encouraged to abandon them.

Once a child knows an algorithmic procedure the only method of developing skill with the procedure is through practice, preferably with the guidance of a concerned teacher. How to do this effectively and efficiently is a problem that has plagued teachers ever since there have been schools. Alleviating these difficulties is a goal worth reaching for. As J.D. Williams wrote:

> Any information bearing upon the question of how the difficulty of learning (the calculative procedures of arithmetic) can be surmounted must be welcome—if only because the more effectively we teach arithmetic, the more time we shall have for teaching the other parts of mathematics (1971, 49).

twenty-one

fractions:

bridging the
understanding gap

Some children develop an understanding of mathematical concepts by a fortuitous set of circumstances, some by means of a carefully planned sequence of instruction, and some do not develop an understanding at all. For all children, but especially for those having trouble remembering and using mathematics, teaching to develop understanding is a good idea. "Young minds need and seek meaning, and failing to find anything but meaningless symbol patterns in our textbook teaching, soon resign themselves to boredom, fantasy, and the memorizing of tricks and gimmicks to be used in passing tests" (Olson 1969, 280). Memorizing tricks is no help when problems must be solved in or out of school.

Teaching for understanding requires a great deal of time and dedication. The teacher must formulate clear and appropriate instructional objectives, facilitate discussions among learners, and buy or make materials that encourage children's exploration and reflection. In this process, because learning fractions is a complex task, patience and creativity are not only virtues but are also necessities.

Before children can understand fractions, they must believe (though may not be able to state) that a whole is divisible into a number of parts, that quantity is conserved under such a division, and that the size of each part decreases as the number of equal divisions increases. Only when all these prerequisites are in place is the student ready to begin mastering the complex idea of fractions.

A fraction can describe part of a region, part of a set, part of a distance, or a unit of time, or it can be considered as a ratio or a command to divide and/or multiply. The models for fractions found in textbooks are usually of the first type ("Draw an X on the pie that is divided into halves") or the second ("Color half the balls red"). Occasionally rod or number-line models are discussed. Of course, in time-telling units "half past" and "quarter of" are used, though these terms may be built upon rather than taught in this context. Less frequently, and usually at the upper grade levels, fractions are considered as ratios (5 people to 1 car) or as operational commands (to find $\frac{2}{3}$, divide by 3 and multiply by 2) addressed to the student. Whenever possible, all these meanings of fractions should become part of the child's concept of each fraction, but it is confusing to learn all of them at once.

It is also confusing to consider $\frac{1}{2}$, $\frac{3}{5}$, $\frac{2}{7}$, $\frac{1}{9}$, and other fractions simultaneously. Wise teachers will confine initial investigations to halves, fourths, and thirds, especially for students who have experienced problems learning mathematics. Fractions with numerators greater than one or fractions with large denominators are more difficult to comprehend. Because 90 percent of the fractions employed in daily life are $\frac{1}{2}$, $\frac{1}{3}$, and $\frac{1}{4}$ (Wilson and Dalrymple 1937), restricting the study of fractions to these three will not significantly hamper young students and will allow the teacher to pare down the learning task somewhat. If time permits consideration of other fractional parts, this is all to the good, but a firm but limited body of knowledge is preferable to a vast, unstable jumble.

A classroom in which meaningful learning is a goal should be a laboratory for exploration and discovery of the physical features of the real world and should build on the children's own social and psychological strengths. In the initial study of fractions—as in the initial study of number, geometry, and measurement—there should be minimal stress on pencil-and-paper activities and maximal involvement with real materials. A teacher who wishes to provide a mathematics program based on what is known about how children learn will not rely solely on a standard textbook. By their very nature, books must be on the pictorial—if not the

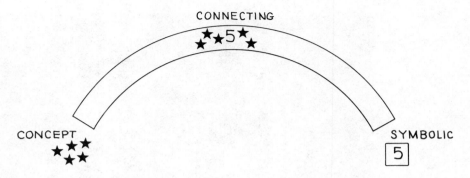

Figure 21–1:   *Workjobs Schema*

abstract—level, and children need much experience with real objects before abstracting relationships from pictures and symbols is appropriate; this is especially true when the topic is as difficult as fractions. Even for nine-year-olds who adapt readily to the demands of a standard curriculum, the connections among fractional models, words, and symbols is only weakly established (Post 1981).

Children who learn to manipulate fractions without attaching meaning to the symbols "are often bewildered by any suggestion that they might learn to use arithmetic in the quantitative problems of real life" (Olson 1969, 276). This statement is especially true for the child who learns mathematics only with much difficulty. Because fractions in real-life situations occur in many guises, they must be taught in many situations. Both continuous (number line or parts of a region) and discrete (sets of objects) models should be included in the instructional sequence. In considering region models, it is important to use rectangular as well as circular regions; although "fraction pies" do depict fractions as part of a region, that is not all of the story. But again, not everything needs to be nor can be taught at once.

The parts-of-a-set model is often familiar to the students and is especially appropriate for initial lessons. It is serendipitous that there are appealing materials useful in the development of this fraction concept, many of which were originally developed to illuminate for children the meaning of number or of the four whole-number operations. For example, *Workjobs II* by the late Mary-Baratta-Lorton (1979), adapts beautifully to the study of fractions. Her philosophy, presented schematically in Figure 21–1, can serve as an especially useful guide in the development of fraction concepts.

Figure 21–2:   Chicken and corn

Variety and the stimulus for conversation is found in the set of *Workjobs II* boxes. Stress on individual decision making is also a feature. For example, a child can be given eight copies of the mat for Chickens (Figure 21–2) and eight bags each containing an even number of pieces of large field corn. After sharing the corn between the two pans, the child can be asked to describe the sharing process to the teacher, aide, or peer. When the child is ready for it, a suggestion might be given by an adult to record in some permanent way such findings as ($\frac{1}{2}$ of 6 = 3 or $\frac{6}{2}$=3. Language-experience charts are a natural extension of this activity and lead easily to small-group discussions.

Conversations arise spontaneously as children being to interact with the *Workjobs II* material. Oral descriptions might include statements such as the following.

Three pieces of corn is half of six pieces of corn.
I put only half as much corn in this chicken's dish as I did in that chicken's dish.
One-third of the corn is in one dish; two-thirds is in the other.
Two corns are here; four corns in all. That means half the corns are in this dish.
Three of the corns are in this dish. That's three out of four. I can write it like this: $\frac{3}{4}$.

Taping these descriptions for later playback will be fun for teacher and student alike.

At first the children should be encouraged to manipulate the materials without worrying about describing the manipulations in numerals. Later the children might match the mats with cards that have fractions written on them. Still later, students might use symbols or equations they have written to describe what they did in fraction books. They may even want to illustrate for a classroom display a variety of ways to show ½ and ¼. As always, teacher assessment of a child's readiness to progress to a new level of learning is crucial.

It is important to remember that children who learn the parts-of-a-set model may not be able to tranfer this learning automatically to the other models for fractions—part-of-a-line and part-of-a-region models. Although it is fairly easy for an adult to abstract ½ from these diverse situations, it is not necessarily so for a child. Some materials that might help students develop the part-of-a-line notion are yarn strips, string licorice, and twine. These can be cut or folded into two or four equal pieces quite easily. Cutting them into three or six equal pieces, on the other hand, is quite difficult.

Materials that help students develop the concept of a fraction as part of a region include graham crackers, folded paper squares, fraction bar sets, colored rods, and paper (or real) pies and cakes. Because it is important in the development of concepts to vary all nonessential traits, many shapes should be used as regions. Variety is the meat as well as the spice of concept formation. But the teacher seeking to help children develop meanings will want to balance novelty and comfortable familiarity of materials during the instructional sequence. Initially, asking children to cut a square or circular region in half will often result in two pieces that are far from equal in size. Discussion about the meaning of one-half (one of two equal parts) may elicit a better response on the next trial, but if the child is still unable to conserve parts of a whole, it may not elicit a better response. Again, teacher patience, personal experience with a variety of materials, and discussion with other children are called for.

In the teaching of fractions, teachers must have great patience with their young students. The understanding of fractions is a very difficult concept, and its mastery will not be a quick process. Building a solid foundation for later learning, however, is the gram of prevention worth far more than a kilogram of cure!

twenty-two

a few final words

An old saying goes, "Well begun is half done." Although "half" is a trifle overoptimistic, it is true that a good beginning will go a long way towards making mathematics a meaningful subject. Neither in mathematics nor in any other area can meanings be handed to a student. Each must develop an individual conceptual network. A child can be helped in this task by interaction with peers and adults and by manipulative objects in the physical environment, but the process requires the reflective activity of his or her own brain; playing or listening is not enough. To build such a schema, the child must notice similarities and differences, varying attributes and invariants, essential and nonessential features, and she or he must use this data to construct a useable system of mathematics. Despite the importance of knowing one's facts, it is the development of concepts that is fundamental to the study of mathematics. Solid development of concepts is fundamental to problem solving, and problem solving is the heart of mathematics.

problem solving—the ultimate goal

Because of disproportionate emphasis on computation, schoolchildren who are able to use the four fundamental processes in arithmetics with skill and accuracy often fail to apply these processes correctly in problems

(Hildreth 1947, 786). This state is as true now as the day it was written. Now, as then, many children know the number facts well and are able to follow the step-by-step procedures of the standard algorithms yet cannot use this knowledge when presented with a problem in a textbook or in real life. Identified by NCTM as the prime focus of mathematics education for the decade, problem solving requires the synthesis of many bits of information, the analysis of a situation complete with extraneous information, and the application of procedures that must be chosen from a wide repertoire. The chances of making at least one mistake within the process are legion. It is no wonder that problem solving is so difficult.

Research on problem solving has been copious (Suydam 1982), and out of it some guideposts for teachers have emerged. Teachers who wish to help children develop problem-solving ability should provide early and frequent practice in this area. During the elementary-school years, teachers should ensure that children attain ready recall of the number facts and that they can use an efficient algorithm for each of the four operations. They should also ensure that children have the vocabulary necessary to translate a problem into a helpful format, that they can identify what is given and what is needed, and that they have a sufficient knowledge of each operation so they know when it is needed. In order to solve problems, children need facility with facts and operations and a way to communicate the answer to others. They need all the knowledge that has been previously discussed in this book and lots of practice in putting it all together.

This practice need not always include all the steps of the problem. Sometimes children might simply say how they would solve it or identify the "givens." Often they can be asked to make up a story to go with a number sentence such as $3-2=1$ and to use materials such as the *Workjob II* kits to illustrate the story. They can work in pairs, with one person making up the number sentence and the other acting out the story. Groups can discuss daily situations that involve numbers—how many cars will be needed for a class trip, how many people are present that day and how many absent, how much punch will be needed for the Valentine's Day party. An alert teacher will notice hundreds of ways to include important problem-solving practice throughout the school year. The following advice is as fresh as today's daisy.

> Traditionally, teachers find it more expedient to solve children's natural problems for them rather than to allow them time to think through the problems themselves. This is comparable to the busy mother's

saying, "It's easier to pick up Sally's clothes for her than to wait till she does it herself." Like the blackboard decorations that the teacher does "after school" to surprise the children when they return in the morning, such limited number thinking as this required in the typical lower grade classroom is done by the teacher herself—"the number of sticks of chalk we need," "the cost of the lunch," or "the scores in the games." Invaluable opportunities to teach numbers in the most profitable way are lost (Hildreth 1957, 475).

Problem solving demands the use of reasoning. Beginning with "simple" exercises in classification and seriation, children exposed to a curriculum based on how children learn are developing more mature thinking skills and learning that they can succeed. Not everyone believes in the importance of the affective domain in education. Those of us who do, however, see the development of the idea of personal competence as essential to a successful learning career—and a happier one.

The teacher must be conscious that reasoning takes *time*, which is one of the most precious gifts you can give children, and it is free. When one of the students in my methods course was told the research of Mary Budd Rowe revealed that teachers waited on the average less than one second between asking for a response and expecting an answer she said, "That's not much time to think, is it?" No, it isn't. Especially when we want children to explore relatively new mental territory, we must be certain we exercise patience.

The prime goal of mathematics instruction is development of the ability to solve problems presented in real life. Do not mistake the ability to do a subtraction example well with the ability to know when subtraction is needed, estimate the answer, and arrive at a correct solution. Likewise, do not believe that children who can reason well but who have only a weak recall of number facts or the ways to process numerals will be great problem solvers. They need it all.

the total teacher

Many adults and children are victims of an uncomfortable mental state, far reaching in its consequences, that is called math anxiety. Elementary-school teachers may suffer from it because, during their own school days, mathematics was taught in a way that was confusing, incorrect, or both. Because what they studied made no sense, they became convinced that it had no relevance to present life and little promise of being useful in the future. The result of math anxiety is often a teacher who will not deviate from the textbook, is "busy" when a child asks for help, and dreads compiling the figures for monthly reports. Any teacher can, however, add to his or her own ease and effectiveness by taking steps to learn the mathematics underlying what is taught in the elementary curriculum. The results in feelings of confidence and competence will repay the effort.

Mathematics at the early childhood level need not be dull. Especially in the early years, mathematics time can be challenging and exciting and rewarding for everyone—teacher and students alike. Once a teacher knows what should be taught, the "how" is limited only by that teacher's creativity.

characteristics of a good program

A teacher probably has a good mathematics program if:

1. Children are enthusiastically making their own number discoveries.
2. Each child has an opportunity to proceed at his or her own rate.
3. The focus is on the development of meanings rather than on just the memorization of number facts and procedures.
4. Children drill only on what they already understand.
5. Children set challenges for themselves and enjoy trying to meet them.
6. Children are developing power in the use of the numerical and measurement processes.
7. Children show an awareness of the need for and a desire of applying mathematics in their daily lives.
8. The teacher approaches math lessons in a cheerful frame of mind.

Considering the cumulative nature of mathematics, the breadth and depth of its topics, and its importance in the daily life of almost every person, it is imperative that instruction be effective, efficient, and enjoyable. That this has not been the case in the school careers of hosts of adults from 18 to 80 is all too evident. Many of them, and perhaps you yourself, failed to learn this essential subject in any meaningful way and now lack competence and/or confidence in its application. Often, the problem was not with the learner, but with the teacher. As you begin your teaching career, you can take steps to structure an environment that fosters the ability of your students to relate joyfully to the world of number and measurement.

How then, shall one present mathematics to the young child? It should be presented in ways that will acknowledge the child as a young but thinking person. "The role of the adult in the classroom is threefold: It is the role of a provider of material and stimuli as well as of a 'climate' which allows for individual and social growth, of a mediator of experience who looks on every aspect of children's living as a means of learning, and of a teacher whose professional knowledge and skill enables her to teach at the moment of willingness and ability to learn (Brearley, et al 1970, 184)." The teacher who reaches for this lofty goal will have met the challenge presented by those twenty-five or so young children and will have helped the promise of each child unfold. Building on the child's earliest experiences, such teachers will nourish and nurture the child's innate sense of wonder and develop in each the ability to use mathematics creatively.

Each teacher develops a philosophy of education, either consciously or unconsciously, and this philosophy effects everything the teacher does and says, from allotment of time to the type of materials provided in the classroom. It is my firm conviction that children learn mathematics best by receiving sensory impressions from the world, relating these to past experiences and thoughts, and coordinating the new and the old into a personally structured whole. This belief has prompted every sentence in this text. Every teacher must come to an equally firm conviction and develop a teaching style consistent with it. This is not an easy task, nor one that will be accomplished during the preservice years or even the early years of teaching. Being aware the challenge is there, however, is the first step towards meeting it.

Teaching young children is a difficult task, and teaching mathematics is also difficult, so teaching young children mathematics can sometimes seem all too heavy a burden. Persevere—the rewards are worth the effort. "The place to improve the world is first in one's own heart and head and hands, and then work outward from there" (Pirsig 1975, 291). You have been working diligently for several years improving your knowledge and skills and learning about how children grow and develop. You have been learning the importance of your task, and it is hoped that you have come to care that you do it well. The world is waiting for you.

> We shall not cease from exploration
> And the end of all our exploring
> Will be to arrive where we started
> And know the place for the first time.
>   T.S. Eliot

appendices

appendix a

Expectations of Experienced Kindergarten Teachers

Clearly kindergarten competencies

	Percent of children reaching competency			
Competency	0–25	26–50	51–75	76–100
Rationally count to 20	2	3	13	82*
Recognition of numerals to 10	0	1	7	92
Identify sets of 0, 1, 2, 3, 4, and 5	0	3	8	89
Identify sets of 6, 7, 8, 9, and 10	3	4	17	76
Write numerals 0–5 in order	2	2	4	92
Write numerals 6–10 in order	1	4	9	86
Identification of circle, square, rectangle, and triangle	0	2	4	94
Identification of a circle, its inside and outside	2	5	12	81

*   This is read: 82% of the teachers reported that at the end of the school year, 76–100% of their children could rationally count to 20. This percentage added to the next lower figure indicates that most all children do well on this competency.

Questionable kindergarten competencies

	Percent of children reaching competency			
Competency	0–25	26–50	51–75	76–100
Write numerals in order to 20	13	17	37	33*
Identify sets for one more and one less	5	10	39	46
Join 2 sets to form sums to 5	7	16	30	47
Join 2 sets to form sums to 10	17	21	30	32
Separate 2 sets to form differences from 5	23	23	22	32
Add numerals to sums of five	12	22	26	40
Tell time on the hour	15	20	31	34
Locate a day of the month on the calendar	9	18	33	40
Identify penny, nickel, and dime	6	18	34	42

*   This is read: 33% of the teachers reported that at the end of the school year 76–100% of their children could write numerals in order to 20.

Clearly not kindergarten competencies

	Percent of children reaching competency			
Competency	0–25	26–50	51–75	76–100
Write numerals as sets of tens and ones	66*	15	12	7
Rationally count to 100	25	22	37	16
Recognition of numerals to 50	19	31	37	13
Identify halves, fourths, and thirds	40	37	18	5
Count by twos to 20	57	24	14	5
Separate 2 sets to form differences from 10	34	24	24	18
Add numerals to sums of 10	27	22	29	22
Subtract numerals to form differences from 5	35	25	17	23
Subtract numerals to form differences from 10	48	23	21	8
Read a thermometer	49	27	20	4
Identify odd numbers to 20	64	17	14	5

*   This is read: 66% of the teachers reported that at the end of the school year only 0–25% of their children could write numerals as sets of tens and ones.

(From Kurtz 1978)

appendix b
Some Suppliers of Math Resources

ABC School Supply/437 Armour Circle/Atlanta, GA 30324

Activity Resources/Box 4875/Haywood, CA 94540

Addison-Wesley/2725 Sand Hill Road/Menlo Park, CA 94025

Childcraft Education Corporation/3135 Ridgewood Rd., NW/Atlanta, GA 30327

Creative Publications/P.O. Box 10328/Palo Alto, CA 94303

Cuisenaire Company of America, Inc./12 Church Street/New Rochelle, NY 10805

Curriculum Development Associates/Suite 414/1211 Conn. Ave./Washington, DC 20036

Developmental Learning Materials/One DLM Park/Allen TX 75002

Didax Educational Resources/6 Doulton Place/Peabody, MA 01960

Educat/P.O. Box 2158/Berkeley, CA 94702

Educational Teaching Aids/159 West Kinzie St./Chicago, IL 60610

Environments, Inc./P.O. Box 1348/Beaufort Industrial Park/Beaufort, SC 29902

General Learning Corporation/3 East 54th Street/New York, NY 10022

Ideal School Supply Company/Oak Lawn, IL 60453

Lapine Scientific Co./6013 South Knox Avenue/Chicago, IL 60629

Leicestershire Learning Systems/Chestnutt Street/Lewiston, ME 04240

McGraw-Hill Publishing Company/Webster Division/1221 Avenue of the Americas/New York, NY 10020

Midwest Publications/P.O. Box 448/Pacific Grove, CA 93950

Milton-Bradley Company/Springfield, MA 01101

Mind-Matter Corporation/P.O. Box 345/Danbury, CT 06810

Science Research Associates, Inc./155 N. Wacker Drive/Chicago, IL 60606

Scholastic Magazine/2915 Providence Road/Charlotte, NC 28211

Scott Resources/P.O. Box 2121PR/Ft. Collins, CO 80522

Spectrum/P.O. Box 6607/Bridgewater, NJ 08807

Texas Instruments/P.O. Box 5012/Dallas, TX 75222

Webster McGraw-Hill/1221 Avenue of the Americas, New York, NY 10020

And, of course:

NCTM/1906 Assocation Drive/Reston, VA 22091

appendix c
Anxious about a Math Word?
Maybe This Glossary Will Help

addend   One of the numbers added to determine a sum. (In the equation $4 + 7 = 11$, 4 and 7 are addends, 11 is the sum.)

additive inverse   For a given number, the number that can be added to give a sum of 0. (-4 is the additive inverse of $+4$, because $+4 + -4 = 0$.)

algorithm   A step-by-step procedure for performing computations.

altitude of a triangle   The distance between a point on the base and the vertex of the opposite angle, measured along a line that is perpendicular to the base. (The altitude is also referred to as the height of the triangle.)

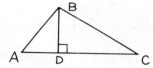

(Segment BD is the altitude in the triangle ABC.)

angle   A figure formed by two rays having a common endpoint (vertex).
An **acute angle** measures less than 90° (Figure 1).
A **right angle** measures 90° (Figure 2).
An **obtuse angle** measures more than 90° and less than 180° (Figure 3).
A **straight angle** measures 180° (Figure 4).

arc   A portion of the edge of a circle between any two points on the circle.

area   The measure of the region inside a closed plane figure. Area is measured in square units.

array   A rectangular arrangement of objects in rows and columns. A 4-by-3 array is shown below.

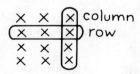

associative property for addition   Whenever a, b and b are real numbers, $a + (b+c) = (a+b) + c$.

associative property for multiplication   Whenever a, b, and c are real numbers, $a \times (b \times c) = (a \times b) \times c$.

base   1.   A side of a geometric figure.
2.   Standard grouping of a numeration system. (If a numeration system groups objects by fives, 23$_5$ is a base-5 numeral meaning 2 fives and 3 ones.)
3.   A number used as a repeated factor, as the 7 in 7^2.

binary operation   Any operation involving two numbers.

bisect   To divide into two congruent parts.

cardinal number   The number of elements in a set (If A $= \{6, 7, 8\}$, $n(A) = 3$)

chord   A line segment having endpoints on a circle.

circle   A simple closed curve all of whose points are equidistant from a given point in the same plane.

circumference   The distance around a circle. (Circumference$=\pi$ x diameter.)

closed figure   A set of points that encloses a region in the same plane; a curve that begins and ends at the same point.

common factor   A whole number that is a factor of two or more numbers. (3 is a factor common to 6, 9, and 12.)

common multiple   A whole number that is a multiple of two or more numbers. (24 is a multiple common to 2, 3, 4, and 6; 12 is their least common multiple.)

commutative property for addition   Whenever a and b are real numbers, $a + b = b + a$.

commutative property of multiplication   Whenever a and b are real numbers, a x $b = b$ x a.

complex fraction   A fraction having a fraction or a mixed numeral as its numerator and/or denominator.

$$(\tfrac{3/5}{1/2} \text{ is a complex faction.})$$

composite number   A number having at least three whole-number factors.

congruent   Two figures of equal size and shape. The symbol $\cong$ means congruent.

coordinates   A pair of numbers that give the location of a point on a plane.

data   A set of scores or other information.

decimal   Pertaining to ten.

decimal system   A numeration system based on grouping by tens.

degree   1.   A unit of measure used in measuring angles. A circle contains 360 degrees.
2.   A unit for measuring temperature.

denominator   The number below the line in a fraction. The denominator in 2/7 is 7.

diagonal   A line segment joining two nonadjacent vertices in a polygon.

difference   The answer in a subtraction problem.

digit   The basic symbols in a numeration system. In the Hindu-Arabic system there are ten digits: 0, 1, 2, 3, 4, 5, 6, 7, 8, 9.

disjoint sets   Sets having no members in common.

distributive property for multiplication over addition   If a, b, and c are real numbers, then $a(b+c) = ab + ac$.

dividend   A number that is to be divided in a division problem. (In $23\sqrt{1980}$, 1980 is the dividend.)

divisibility   A number is divisible by a given number if the quotient is a whole number.

division   The operation of finding a missing factor when the product and one factor are known.

divisor   The factor used in a division problem for the purpose of finding the missing factor.
$$\text{(In } 23\sqrt{1980}\text{ , 23 is the divisor.)}$$

edge   A line segment formed by the intersection of two faces of a geometric space figure.

element   A member of a set. $\{\quad\}$

empty set   A set having no elements; also called a null set. An empty set is represented like this:

endpoint   A point at the end of a line segment or ray.

equation   A mathematical sentence stating that two expressions are equal.

equilateral   Having sides of the same length. (Figure ABC is an equilateral triangle; all its sides are the same length.)

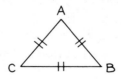

equivalent fractions   Fractions that name the same number.

equivalent sets   Sets having the same number of members.

even number   One of the set of whole numbers having 2 as a factor.

expanded notation   A method of writing a numeral as the sum of its place-value components. ($5327 = 5000 + 300 + 20 + 7$)

exponent   A numeral telling how many times a number is to be used as a factor. (In 6^3, the exponent is 3. 6^3 means $6 \times 6 \times 6$, or 216.)

factor   A number that can be divided evenly into the given number. Two factors of 54 are 6 and 9.

finite set   A set having a finite number of elements.

flip   To turn over a geometric figure. The size or shape of the figure does not change.

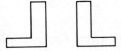

fraction   A name for a numeral written in the form a/b, $b/ = 0$; a is the numerator and b is the denominator.

function   A set of ordered pairs of numbers such that for each first element there is a unique second element determined by some rule.

gram   A standard unit for measuring weight (mass) in the metric system.

graph   A drawing showing relationships between sets.

greatest common factor   The largest number that is a factor of two other numbers. (6 is the greatest common factor of 18 and 24.)

grid   A set of horizontal and vertical lines spaced uniformly.

horizontal   A line that runs parallel to a base line.

hypotenuse   The longest side of a right triangle. It is located opposite the right angle.

identity element for addition   Zero is the identity element for addition. If b is any number, then $b + 0 = b$.

identity element for multiplication   One is the identity element for multiplication. If a is any number, then $a \times 1 = a$.

improper fraction   A fraction having a numerator equal to or greater than the denominator, therefore naming a number equal to or greater than one.

inequality   A number sentence showing that two groups of numerals stand for different numbers.

The signs $<$, $>$, $/ =$ show inequality ($7 - 5 < 12 - 9$).

infinite set   A set having an unlimited number of members.

integer   Any member of the set of positive or negative counting numbers and zero.

$$\ldots -4, -3, -2, -1, 0, 1, 2, 3, 4 \ldots$$

intersection   1.   The point at which two lines (or planes) meet.

2.   The set of elements that two or more given sets have in common. The symbol for intersection is

meter   The basic unit of linear measurement in the metric system. A meter is a little longer than a yard.

metric system   A system of measurement based on the decimal system.

mixed numeral   A numeral that includes a whole number and a fraction number or a whole number and a decimal.

multiple   The product of a whole number and any other whole number. (12 is a multiple of 3 because $3 \times 4 = 12$.)

multiplicative inverse   For any given number a, the number that will yield a product of 1. The multiplicative inverse of ¾ is ⁴⁄₃ because $⁴⁄₃ \times ¾ = 1$.

natural number   A member of the set $\{1, 2, 3, 4 \ldots\}$.

negative integer   One of a set of counting numbers that is less than zero.

nondecimal numerals   Numerals representing numbers in a system having a base other than 10. (23_4 is a base-4 numeral.)

number   A mathematical idea concerning the amount contained in a set.

number line   A line that has numbers corresponding to points along it.

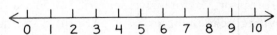

numeral   A symbol used to represent or name a number.

numeration system   A system of symbols used to express numbers.

numerator   The number above the line in a fraction. In the fraction ¾, 3 is the numerator.

odd number   A whole number not evenly divisible by 2.

ordered pair   A pair of numbers whose *order* of presentation is significant.

ordinal number   A number telling the place of an item in an ordered set. *Sixth* is an ordinal number.

one-to-one correspondence   Two sets A and B are in one-to-one correspondence if every member of set A can be matched to one and only one member of set B.

palindrome   A number that reads the same forward and backward. (323 and 87678 are palindromic numbers.)

parallel lines   Lines in the same plane that do not intersect.

parallelogram   A quadrilaterial whose opposite sides are parallel.

percent   A comparison of a number with 100. (43 compared to 100 is 43 percent.)

perimeter   The distance around the outside of a closed figure.

perpendicular lines   Two lines in the same plane that intersect at right angles.

place value   The value assigned to each position in a numeral.

plane   The set of all points on a flat surface that extends indefinitely in all directions.

plane figure   A set of points in the same plane enclosing a region.

point   An exact location in space.

polygon   A simple, closed plane figure having line segments as sides.

polyhedron   A space figure formed by intersecting plane surfaces called faces.

positive integer   A counting number greater than zero.

prime number   A number greater than 1 that has only itself and 1 as factors.

probability   A study of the likelihood that an event will occur.

product   The answer in a multiplication problem.

proportion   A statement of equality between two ratios. (e.g., $\frac{3}{7} = \frac{9}{21}$)

protractor   An instrument used for measuring angles.

pythagorean theorem   A proposition stating that in a right triangle the sum of the squares of the two shorter sides is equal to the square of the third side.

quadrilateral   A four-sided polygon.

quotient   The answer in a division problem.

radius   A straight line segment having one endpoint in the center of the circle and the other on the circle.

ratio   A comparion of two numbers expressed as a/b.

rational number   A number that can be expressed in the form a/b where a and b are integers and $b/ = 0$.

ray   A portion of a line extending from one endpoint indefinitely in one direction.

real number   A member of the set of numbers that is the union of the set of the rational numbers and the irrational numbers.

reciprocals   A pair of numbers whose product is 1.

rectangle   A parallelogram having four right angles.

region   The set of all points in the interior or on the boundary of a closed curve.

relation   A set of ordered pairs.

replacement set   A set of numbers that could replace a variable in a number sentence.

sequence   A series of numbers ordered according to a pattern.

set   A collection of items (called members or elements).

similar   Geometric figures having angles of the same size.

simple closed curve or figure   A closed curve whose path does not intersect itself. (The figures below are simple closed curves.)

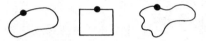

skew lines   Lines that are not in the same plane and do not intersect.

slide   Moving a figure without turning or flipping it. The shape or size of a figure is not changed by a slide.

solution set   the set of replacements for the variable in a number sentence which make the statement true.

space figure   A figure consisting of a set of points lying in two or more planes.

square   A rectangle whose sides are all congruent.

square root   A number that when multiplied by itself yields a given product. ($\sqrt{25} = 5$ and -5 because $5 \times 5 = 25$ and $-5 \times -5 = 25$.)

subset   Any member of a set, or any combination of the members of a set.

subtraction   The operation of finding a missing addend when one addend and the sum are known.

sum   The answer in an addition problem resulting from the combination of two addends.

surface   A region lying on one plane.

surface area   The space covered by a plane region or by the faces of a space figure.

symmetric figure   A figure having two halves that are reflections of one another. A line of symmetry divides the figure into two congruent parts. (The figures illustrated below are symmetric.)

tangent   A line that touches a figure at one point and has all its other points outside the figure.
GH is tangent to the circle at point X.
OX is a radius of the circle.
COD is a diameter.
BQ is a chord.
BD is an arc.

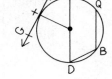

trapezoid   A quadrilateral having only two parallel sides.

triangle   A three-sided polygon. The sum of the angles in a triangle
is 180°.   An **acute triangle** has all three angles less than 90°.

An **isosceles triangle** has at least two congruent sides.

An **obtuse triangle** has one angle greater than 90° angle.

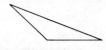

A **right triangle** has one 90°.

A **scalene triangle** has no two sides that are congruent.

turn   A move in geometry that involves turning but not flipping a figure. The size or shape of the figure is not changed by a turn.

union of sets   A set containing the combined members of two or more sets. (∪ is the symbol for union.)

unit   1.   The first whole number.

2.   A determined quantity used as a standard for measurement.

variable   A symbol in a number sentence that could be replaced by a number. (In $3 + x = 9$, x is the variable.)

venn diagram   A pictorial means of representing sets and their union or intersection.

$$A = \{g, f, b, t, i, x, m\}$$
$$B = \{b, i, t, y, a, d, c\}$$
$$A \cup B = \{a, b, c, d, y, i, t, f, m, g, x\}$$
$$A \cap B = \{b, i, t\}$$

vertical   A line that is perpendicular to a horizontal baseline.

volume   The measure of capacity or space enclosed by a space figure.

whole number   A member of the set $\{0, 1, 2, 3, 4, \ldots\}$.

X-axis   The horizontal number line on a coordinate grid.

Y-axis   The vertical number line on a coordinate grid.

zero   The number of members in an empty set.

A Diagram of the Real-Number System

N: natural numbers

W: whole numbers

I: integers

R: rational numbers

R#: real numbers

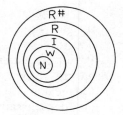

appendix d
Some Psychological Terms: Applications in the Math Classroom

This glossary gives a superficial introduction to some of the psychological terms with application to the mathematics classroom. For each term, sources for further reading are given.

behavior modification   A contemporary extension of Skinnerian psychology, "behavior mod" is an attempt to change or eradicate behavior through a fixed schedule of reinforcement of desired behavior. In using this technique, a teacher liberally praises the child who is "caught being good." Rewards are given at first for quite distant approximations of the desired behavior. Rewards are gradually given less freely and less often until they are extinguished completely. The rate of this extinction of reward is dependent on the rate of behavior adaptation by the child. The technique has been successfully used in such diverse situations as toilet training, increasing attending behavior, and improving pronunciation in foreign languages. (*Readings in Behavior Modification* 1978)

Bruner's hierarchy of modes   Jerome Bruner has postulated that children learn mathematical content best if they work first with real objects (the concrete or enactive mode), then with pictures of objects (the iconic or pictorial mode), and finally with abstract symbols (the symbolic mode). In learning to add, Bruner would say, a child must first work with blocks, beans, or other real objects and then with worksheets containing pictures; only when he or she can perform successfully in both of these modes should problems of the type $2+3=5$ be assigned. (Bruner 1966)

classical conditioning   Pavlov's experiments with dogs were the genesis of his theory of conditioning. In classical conditioning, a natural response to a stimulus is paired with a neutral stimulus. Pavlov presented his dogs with meat as a bell was rung. The dog's natural response was to emit saliva. After repeated presentations of the meat and bell together, the sound of the bell alone was enough to produce the saliva. Many children have "lucky" tokens they carry because something good has happened to them in the past when they had the token in their pockets. A baby will drool as a bib is tied around the neck because this has on many occasions signalled the beginning of a meal. A sadistic teacher of math may cause the pupils to dislike the subject. Many sight words are learned through classical conditioning techniques. The word *dog* is presented along with a picture of a dog. After many trials *dog* is presented alone and the child responds to the letters alone. (Longstreth 1968)

Maslow's hierarchy of needs   According to Abraham Maslow, few people obtain their full potential. Environmental blocks and frustrations prevent their being self-actualized. He postulates a hierarchy of human needs progressing from basic needs to growth needs. Before advancing to self-actualization (creativeness, justice, love of others, meeting challenges), the child must have had all basic needs met; that is, he or she must be free from pain, fear, and hunger, must feel safe from physical threat, and finally must have a sense of belongingness and affection from others. When and only when these basic needs are met, the child is able to advance to becoming a creative, spontaneous, learning, caring person. To the math teacher Maslow's hierarchy implies that one cannot expect a child to be motivated to learn long division if he or she is hungry, afraid of being "beaten up" by parents or peers, or feels isolated from the classroom family. (Maslow 1968)

modeling   Based on the words of Bandura, modeling theory emphasizes the role played by the others in determining the child's behavior. The child is most apt to copy the behavior of someone who is perceived as warm, powerful, or physically similar. Models are particularly effective in the area of aggression. Modeling is a potent force for changing or introducing behavior patterns. In the classroom, correct handwriting, posture, and voice tone are often modeled by the teacher. Children with low self-esteem are most susceptible to models but may not always choose models that teachers consider desirable. (Bandura 1963)

negative reinforcement   In contrast to positive reinforcement, negative reinforcement is the removal of an adversive condition. Negative reinforcement, in Skinnerian terms, is *not* punishment. It, too, is a means of increasing the probability of a behavior, in this case by removing something perceived as undesirable. Some typical negative reinforcers are placing fingers in your ears when a loud noise is bothersome, moving your seat away from a classmate who is annoying, taking aspirin for a headache, or using alcohol to boost self-image. If an action removes an unpleasant condition, it is apt to be repeated when the unpleasant condition is again present. In order for a reinforcer to be used, the desired behavior must be elicited. If the desired behavior is not performed, close approximations to it may be rewarded in order to "shape" behavior. (Hill 1963; Skinner 1948, 1968, 1971)

Piaget's cognitive levels   Jean Piaget, a Swiss epistemologist, defines intelligence as the ability to think logically. He postulates that all children pass through the same stages of intellectual growth in the same order. The age at which a child advances to the next higher stage varies according to the genetic and environmental factors peculiar to the child. Intellectual functioning at the different levels is qualitatively different and the change is preceded by a period of disequilibrium during which the child begins to give up former ways of thinking and adopt new ways. The stages (and approximate mental age ranges) are:

sensori-motor:	(0–2 years)
preoperational:	(2–7 years)
concrete operational:	(7–11 years)
formal operational:	(11 years plus)

A child who has not entered the stage of concrete operations is ruled by his or her perceptions and will assert, for example, that a set of four blocks that are spread out contains more blocks than a set of four blocks that are arranged close together, even if he or she can *count* to 4. Until a child is in the concrete operational stage, much traditional first-grade mathematical content is inappropriate. (Phillips 1969)

positive reinforcement   B. F. Skinner defines reinforcement as the presentation of a stimulus that will increase the probability of a given behavior. A positive reinforcer is a stimulus that is perceived by the receiver as good. Some common positive reinforcers (rewards) in the schoolroom are smiles, verbal praise, tokens, and candy. Reinforcers can be used to establish or maintain desired behaviors. In operant conditioning, the reinforcement must follow the desired behavior promptly, consistently, and frequently at first. (Hill 1963; Skinner 1948, 1968, 1971)

Premack principle   David Premack has developed a twist on Skinner's reinforcement scheme. He found that a desirable action A_1 could be used to reinforce a less desirable action A_2. Making A_1 contingent on the performance of A_2 increases the probability of the less preferred action taking place. Teachers use the Premack principle when they say, "You can go to the game corner after you have finished your math paper." A homely use of the Premack principle is the familiar "No dessert unless you finish your carrots." (Sahakian 1970)

punishment   Punishment is the presentation of an adversive stimulus or the removal of a desirable stimulus. It is designed to *decrease* the probability of the punished behavior. Some familiar examples of presentation of an undesirable stimulus are extra worksheets, scolding, and isolation. Some example of deprivation of desirable stimuli are the removal of library or art room privileges and denial of teacher attention. It is not always possible to tell when too much punishment is being employed. Excessive amounts of punishment can produce emotional problems such as anxiety and aggression. (Hill 1963; Skinner 1948, 1968, 1971)

self-fulfilling prophecy   The self-fulfilling prophecy predicts that a person's perception of a state or behavior will somehow cause the state or behavior to be realized. It is a psychological exposition of "If you think you can do it, you can; if you think you are beaten, you are." A girl who feels "dumb" in math may avoid the subject and will in fact learn little math, thus fulfilling her own prophecy. One person's expectation of another's behavior can produce that behavior, probably due to the way in which the perceiver reacts to that person. A teacher who feels a child is bright reacts in such a way that the expectations are confirmed. Rosenthal and Jacobson (1968) is the classic example of research in this area.

appendix e

*Inexpensive Materials Useful for Teaching Mathematics**

Item	*Some Possible Uses*
cartons, boxes, pails, containers, shoeboxes, bowls, jars	measuring volume, surface area; finding geometric shapes; storing materials
pebbles, rocks, shells, buttons, bottle caps, dry beans, macaroni, nails, screws, nuts, cork, washers, pine cones, acorns, rice, marbles, feathers, Styrofoam chips, thread spools, clay	sorting, counting, balancing, weighing, ordering; linear, meass, area, or volume measurement
beans, sand, gravel, plastic tubs	measuring
stapler, staples, brass fasteners, paperclips, file folders, tape, cement glue, felt-tip pens, scissors, labels, pencils, clear shellac, colored paper, colored oaktag, fabric, index cards, spinners	making task cards, models, and games; organizing materials
sets of similar containers in different sizes—toothpaste boxes, mixing bowls, cans, plastic bowls, measuring cups	ordering; finding linear, area, and volume measurements; discovering ratios
ceramic tiles, poker chips, rubber stamps	making patterns, counting, place value
yarn, zippers, string, cord, bias tape	measuring, patterning, seriating
playing cards, dice, dominoes, bingo cards, spinners	making number games, discovering probabilities
adding machine tape	making number lines, finding linear distances
funnels, scoops, eyedroppers, measuring spoons, standard measures (ounce, pint, quart, gallon, gram, liter, foot, yard, meter, inch) tape measures, paperclips	weighing and measuring

*   Adapted by the author from a list originally compiled by Mary Baratta-Lorton.

Item	*Some Possible Uses*
ribbons of different colors, widths, lengths, textures; wooden or plastic figures of animals; buttons; shells; leaves	sorting, attribute games, developing number concepts and basic vocabulary
pegboard and pegs or golf tees	making patterns, showing basic operations, graphing, making charts, counting, making geoboards
newspapers, magazines, catalogs, used adding machine tapes, menus, containers with labels	composing and solving real-life problems
rubber bands of assorted sizes and colors	making geoboard designs, sorting
cardboard tubes, plastic straws, pipe cleaners, spaghetti	finding volume, seriating, discovering geometric properties
mirrors (preferably plastic or metal)	discovering line symmetry and patterns
toothpicks, clay, straws, wire, wirecutters, clear nail polish, thread	mobiles, models
dowels	making an abacus, measuring, seriating
pudding and gelatin mixes, powdered drink mixes	measuring
pressure-sensitive colored squares and circles	making patterns, illustrating the basic facts, graphing, measuring

appendix f
Writing a Lesson Plan

Every good lesson begins with a plan. It must be crystal clear to the teacher what he or she hopes the students will learn and/or be able to do at the end of the instructional sequence. The most important part of the planning process takes place between the ears. Because writing is a way of knowing, however, making a written record of the plan is a good practice for the beginning teacher. Many formats can be used; each teacher will sooner or later find one that meets his or her needs best. One you can start with is included here as Figure F–1.

Any lesson plan should address the questions, "Who are the learners? What will they be learning? *How* will I know if they have learned?" In some cases the questions, "What materials will I need?" or "What else should I include?" must also be answered. The most important part of your lesson plan is the objective, because it is from the objective that all the rest flows. Be sure it is stated clearly in terms of expected student behavior.

Because a major function of the lesson plan is to communicate expectations to someone who fills in for the teacher, it is important to aim for clarity and avoid jargon or cryptic notes. "Do the usual with the next 3 pages of book" isn't likely to help a substitute teacher very much.

Every good lesson incorporates certain, not necessarily distinct, procedures:

Preparation
    Gaining attention
    Informing students of intended learnings
    Stimulating recall

Presentation
    Presenting stimulus materials
    Providing learning guidance

Practice
    Eliciting the performance
    Providing feedback
    Assessing performance
    Enhancing retention and transfer (Gagné and Briggs 1978)

A list of sample teacher activities for each of these events of instruction was generated by the faculty of the School of Education at the University of North Carolina at Wilmington; it can be seen at right. The observant reader will notice that the categories are far from airtight. For instance, passing out a printed outline may gain attention, inform students of the intended learning, stimulate recall, and provide learning guidance. Although the lesson plan should include all nine events of instruction, it may not have nine separate teacher activities. A sample lesson plan can be seen in Figure F–2.

Figure F–1   Sample Lesson Plan Form

Name_____   Date_____
Group_____   Topic_____
Objective:

_____

Activities	Materials	Evaluation

Notes

Figure F–2   Sample Lesson Plan

Name___Ms. Sample_____   Date___Today_____
Group___12 second graders_____   Topic___Multiplication concepts (a, b ≤ 5)
Objectives: Model: arrays
Given concrete materials, the student will construct two different arrays to illustrate multiplication sentences of the type a × b = □ where a, b ≤ 5 and a ≠ b. (Acceptable level of competence, 2 out of 3.)

_____

Activities	Materials	Evaluation
1. Show a "stuff array" on the overhead. Review geoboard activity from yesterday.	stuff graph paper cut into rectangles (l ≤ 5, w ≤ 5) students' number card stacks for multiplication	Teacher observation of student responses to: "Use stuff to make two different arrays showing 3 × 5 (4 × 5, 5 × 2)."
2. Have students place stuff, 1 piece per square, on rectangles of graph paper. Example: :::		
3. Ask students to exchange papers and remove from their stack of number cards all those that describe the array. (Example: 2 × 3 = 6, 3 × 2 = 6).		
4. Circulate among the groups, providing help as necessary.		
5. Repeat steps 2-4 several times.		
6. Repeat steps 2-4 without the use of graph paper.		
7. Present novel examples (a or b = 5) to be constructed.		

Notes

homework: cut pictures of arrays from magazines. Bring in for bulletin board display.

challenge: Draw as many arrays as possible to show 8, 12, and 15.

examples of the events of instruction

1. Gaining attention of the students.
   Ways of gaining attention that might be used by an instructor are:
   a. distributing materials
   b. rearranging the group
   c. changing voice level
   d. using a variety of agreed-upon signals to begin a new activity
   e. asking leading questions
2. Informing the students of the intended learning.
   Ways of informing the students of the intended learning that might be used by an instructor are:
   a. showing examples of the performance that is expected
   b. describing verbally the expected performance
   c. providing written instructions for procedures to be used
   d. engaging the class in a discussion of the intended learning
3. Stimulating recall of prerequisite learnings.
   Ways of stimulating recall of prerequisite learnings that might be used by an instructor are:
   a. discussing topics related to the new learning
   b. asking questions that require thought about topics related to the new learning
   c. structuring a review
   d. providing printed outlines of content related to the new learning topics
4. Presenting the stimulus materials.
   Ways of presenting the stimulus materials that might be used by an instructor are:
   a. lecturing
   b. showing a film
   c. questioning to present a problem situation
   d. assigning specific readings
   e. initiating question-and-answer sessions
5. Providing learning guidance.
   Ways of providing learning guidance that might be used by an instructor are:
   a. sequencing the learning task into steps
   b. asking questions to focus the learner's attention
   c. providing hints to problem solutions
   d. verbally providing the learner with information that is not being recalled

6. Eliciting performance.
   Ways of eliciting performance that might be used by an instructor are:
   a. asking individual students to respond to specific oral questions
   b. requiring completion of learning tasks
   c. providing practice activities and materials
7. Providing feedback about performance correctness.
   Ways of providing feedback about performance correctness that might be used by an instructor are:
   a. giving oral feedback for oral responses
   b. providing learning activities that include a performance that is obvious to the learner
   c. providing answer keys to use in practice work
   d. using nonverbal indicators of satisfaction or dissatisfaction with responses such as a nod or a smile
8. Assessing performance.
   Ways of assessing performance that might be used by an instructor are:
   a. using "objective" tests such as multiple choice
   b. providing several problem situations that require solutions
   c. observing performance during learning situations
   d. providing tasks that require the development of a plan
9. Enhancing retention and transfer.
   Ways of enhancing retention and transfer that might be used by an instructor are:
   a. orally summarizing at the end of instructional sessions
   b. providing activities, materials, or problems that are new to the learner
   c. providing a periodic review of prior learnings
   d. providing a variety of examples of situations in which learnings can be applied
   e. providing learning tasks that differ in the type of activity and topic

appendix g
Commandments for a Math Teacher *

1. Thou shalt create a classroom environment that speaks of a love for thy class and an understanding of how they learn.
2. Thou shalt not teach by worksheets and textbooks alone, nor give ditto after ditto.
3. Thou shalt not ignore a child in need.
4. Thou shalt use many strategies for assessment.
5. Thou shalt have a specific reason for asking thy students to do each assignment.
6. Thou shalt seek to develop the patience of Job and the wisdom of Solomon.
7. Thou shalt forgive and learn from mistakes, both thine and those of thy students.
8. Thou shalt respect thy students and treat them fairly.
9. Thou shalt not limit math to math time alone.
10. Thou shalt provide opportunities for each child to succeed at his or her highest level.
11. Thou shalt not gossip about the progress or lack of progress of the children in thy class.
12. Thou shalt remain calm.
13. Thou shalt not give up.
14. Thou shalt not enter the classroom unprepared.
15. Thou shalt be sure each student has mastery over each skill before attempting the next.
16. Thou shalt not ridicule or terrorize in any way a student learning math.
17. Thou shalt be an enthusiastic teacher, sharing thy joy in learning with thy students.
18. Thou shalt beg, borrow, and steal (just a little!) to provide adequate resources for thy students.
19. Thou shalt continue to study and learn.
20. Thou shalt remember the reasons that brought thee to teaching.

*   Compiled by students in an undergraduate mathematics methods class— University of North Carolina at Wilmington.

appendix h
NCTM/NSCM Ten Basic Skill Areas

Ten Basic Skills Areas

Problem Solving   Learning to solve problems is the principal reason for studying mathematics. Problem solving is the process of applying previously acquired knowledge to new and unfamiliar situations. Solving word problems in texts is one form of problem solving, but students also should be faced with non-textbook problems. Problem-solving strategies involve posing questions, analyzing situations, translating results, illustrating results, drawing diagrams, and using trial and error. In solving problems, students need to be able to apply the rules of logic necessary to arrive at valid conclusions. They must be able to determine which facts are relevant. They should be unfearful of arriving at tentative conclusions and they must be willing to subject these conclusions to scrutiny.

Applying Mathematics to Everyday Situations   The use of mathematics is interrelated with all computation activities. Students should be encouraged to take everyday situations, translate them into mathematical expressions, solve the mathematics, and interpret the results in light of the initial situation.

Alertness to the Reasonableness of Results   Due to arithmetic errors or other mistakes, results of mathematical work are sometimes wrong. Students should learn to inspect all results and to check for reasonableness in terms of the original problem. With the increase in the use of calculating devices in society, this skill is essential.

Estimation and Approximation   Students should be able to carry out rapid approximate calculations by first rounding off numbers. They should acquire some simple techniques for estimating quantity, length, distance, weight, etc. It is also necessary to decide when a particular result is precise enough for the purpose at hand.

Appropriate Computational Skills   Students should gain facility with addition, subtraction, multiplication, and division with whole numbers and decimals. Today it must be recognized that long, complicated computations will usually be done with a calculator. Knowledge of single-digit number facts is essential and mental arithmetic is a valuable skill. Moreover, there are everyday situations which demand recognition of, and simple computation with, common fractions.

Because consumers continually deal with many situations that involve percentage, the ability to recognize and use percents should be developed and maintained.

Geometry   Students should learn the geometric concepts they will need to function effectively in the 3-dimensional world. They should have knowledge of concepts such as point, line, plane, parallel, and perpendicular. They should know basic properties of simple geometric figures, particularly those properties which relate to measurement and problem-solving skills. They also must be able to recognize similarities and differences among objects.

Measurement   As a minimum skill, students should be able to measure distance, weight, time, capacity, and temperature. Measurement of angles and calculations of simple areas and volumes are also essential. Students should be able to perform measurement in both metric and customary systems using the appropriate tools.

Reading, Interpreting, and Constructing Tables, Charts, and Graphs   Students should know how to read and draw conclusions from simple tables, maps, charts, and graphs. They should be able to condense numerical information into more manageable or meaningful terms by setting up simple tables, charts, and graphs.

Using Mathematics to Predict   Students should learn how elementary notions of probability are used to determine the likelihood of future events. They should learn to identify situations where immediate past experience does not affect the likelihood of future events. They should become familar with how mathematics is used to help make predictions such as election forecasts.

Computer Literacy   It is important for all citizens to understand what computers can and cannot do. Students should be aware of the many uses of computers in society, such as their use in teaching/learning, financial transactions, and information storage and retrieval. The "mystique" surrounding computers is disturbing and can put persons with no understanding of computers at a disadvantage. The increasing use of computers by government, industry, and business demands an awareness of computer uses and limitations.

appendix i

All You Will Need to Know About Metric (For Your Everyday Life)

Metric is based on decimal system   The metric system is simple to learn. For use in your everyday life you will need to know only ten units. You will also need to get used to a few new temperatures. Of course, there are other units which most persons will not need to learn. There are even some metric units with which you are already familiar: those for time and electricity are the same as you use now.

Basic units:

Meter: a little longer than a yard (about 1.1 yards)
Liter: a little larger than a quart (about 1.06 quarts)
Gram: about the weight of a paperclip

Common Prefixes   *(to be used with basic units)*

Milli: one-thousandth (0.001)
Centi: one-hundredth (0.01)
Kilo: one-thousand times (1000)

For example:

1000	= 1 meter
100 centimeters	= 1 meter
1000 meters	= 1 kilometer

Other Commonly Used Units

Millimeter: 0.001 meter   diameter of paperclip wire
Centimeter: 0.01 meter   width of a paperclip (about 0.4 inch)
Kilometer: 1000 meters   somewhat further than ½ mile (about 0.6 mile).
Kilogram: 1000 grams   a little more than 2 pounds (about 2.2 pounds)
Milliliter: 0.001 liter   five of them make a teaspoon

Other Useful Hints

Hectare: about 2½ acres
Tonne: about one ton
Temperature: degrees Celsius are used

Appendix I con't

DO-IT-YOURSELF TABLE FOR COOKING

Approximate Solid and Liquid Measurements

Metric	English
1 liter	4¼ cups
1 deciliter (dl)	½ cup (scant)
2 deciliters (dl)	1 cup (scant)
240 cubic centimeters (cc)	1 cup
5 cubic centimeters (cc)	1 teaspoon
5 milliliters (ml)	1 teaspoon
15 cubic centimeters (cc)	1 tablespoon
1 liter (1)	34 ounces
28 grams (g)	1 ounce
450 grams (g)	1 pound
1 kilogram (kg)	2.2 pounds

Approximate Temperature Equivalents for Baking:

°F	°C	Description
250	120	Very slow oven
325	160	Slow oven
350	175	Moderate oven
400	205	Hot oven
450	230	Very hot oven

references

Ashlock, Robert B. 1966. "Planning Mathematics Instruction for Four- and Five-Year-Olds." *Arithmetic Teacher* 13: 397–400.

———. 1981. *Error Patterns in Computation*. 3d ed. Columbus, Ohio: Charles E. Merrill.

Bandura, Albert, and R.H. Walters. 1963. *Social Learning and Personality Development*. New York: Holt, Rinehart and Winston.

Baratta-Lorton, Mary. 1975. *Workjobs for Parents*. Menlo Park, Calif.: Addison-Wesley.

———. 1976. *Mathematics Their Way*. Menlo Park, Calif: Addison-Wesley.

———. 1979. *Workjobs II*. Menlo Park, Calif.: Addison-Wesley.

Barbe, W.B., and Joseph Renzulli. 1975. *The Psychology and Education of the Gifted*. New York: Irvington Publishers.

Barron, Linda. 1979. *Mathematics Experiences for the Early Childhood Years*. Columbus, Ohio: Charles E. Merrill.

Beard, Ruth M. 1969. *An Outline of Piaget's Developmental Psychology for Students and Teachers*. New York: Basic Books.

Birch, Herbert G., and Joan Dye Gussow. 1970. *Disadvantaged Children: Health, Nutrition and School Failure*. New York: Harcourt, Brace and World.

Bongard, M. 1970. *Pattern Recognition*. New York: Spartan Books.

Bradford, E.J.G. 1925. "Suggestion, Reasoning and Arithmetic." *Forum of Education* 3: 3–12.

Brearley, Molly, et al. 1970. *The Teaching of Young Children*. New York: Schocken Books.

Brownell, William H. 1941. "The Evaluation of Learning in Arithmetic." In *Arithmetic in General Education*. Sixteenth Yearbook of the National Council of Teachers of Mathematics. Washington, D.C.: The Council.

———. 1944. "The Progressive Nature of Learning in Mathematics." *Mathematics Teacher* 37: 147–157.

———. 1947. "The Place of Meaning in the Teaching of Arithmetic." *Elementary School Journal* 47: 256–265.

Brownell, William H., and Charlotte B. Chazal. 1935. "The Effect of Premature Drill in Third Grade Arithmetic." *Journal of Educational Research* 29: 17–20.

Brueckner, Leo J. 1930. *Diagnostic and Remedial Teaching in Arithmetic*. Chicago: John C. Winston.

Bruner, Jerome S. 1960. "On Learning Mathematics." *Mathematics Teacher* 53: 610–619.

———. 1966. *Towards a Theory of Instruction*. Cambridge: The Belknap Press.

Buckingham, B.R. 1935. "Informational Arithmetic." In *The Teaching of Arithmetic*. Tenth Yearbook of the National Council of Teachers of Mathematics. New York: Bureau of Publications, Teachers College, Columbia University.

Burns, Paul C. 1970. "Development of Elementary School Mathematics Teaching in the United States." *Arithmetic Teacher* 17: 428–437.

Burton, Grace M. 1973. *Variations in the Ontogeny of Linear Patterns Among Young Children*. Ph.D. diss., University of Connecticut, Storrs.

————. 1978. "Helping Parents Help Their Children Prepare for the Study of Mathematics." *Arithmetic Teacher* 25(8): 12–14.

————. 1979. "Getting Comfortable with Mathematics." *Elementary School Journal* 79: 129–135.

————. Forthcoming. "Teaching the Most Basic Basic." *Arithmetic Teacher*.

Burton, Grace M., and J. Dan Knifong. 1980. "Definitions for Prime Numbers." *Arithmetic Teacher* 27(6): 44–47.

————. 1982. "Learning the Number Facts: It Doesn't Need to be Frustrating." *Elementary School Journal* 83: 149–154.

————. 1981. "Helping Children Understand Addition." *Academic Therapy* 16: 481–491.

Callahan, Leroy G., and Vincent J. Glennon. 1975. *Elementary School Mathematics: A Guide to Current Research*. 4th ed. Washington, D.C.: ASCD.

Carson, G. St. L. 1913. *Essays on Mathematical Education*. Boston: Ginn and Co.

Cajori, Florian. 1890. *The Teaching and History of Mathematics in the United States*. Washington, D.C.: Government Printing Office.

————. 1928. *A History of Mathematical Notations*. Vol. 1. Chicago: Open Court.

Colburn, Warren: 1821. *An Arithmetic on the Plan of Pestalozzi*. Boston: Cummings and Hilliard.

————. 1970. "Teaching of Arithmetic." In *Readings in the History of Mathematics Education*, edited by James K. Bidwell and Robert F. Classon. Washington, D.C.: National Council of Teachers of Mathematics, 24–37.

Coxford, Arthur F., Jr. 1963. "Piaget, Number and Measurement." *Arithmetic Teacher* 10: 419–427.

Cubberley, Ellwood P. 1919. *Public Education in the United States*. Boston: Houghton Mifflin.

Davidson, Patricia. 1974. *Chip Trading Activities Teachers Guide*. Fort Collins, Colo.: Scott Resources.

————. 1979. "The Guest Room." *Virginia Mathematics Teacher* 5: 3–8.

Davies, H.B. 1978. "A Seven-Year-Old's Subtraction Technique." *Mathematic Teaching* 83: 15–16.

deRegniers, Beatrice Schenk; Eva Moore; and Mary Michaels White. 1969. *Poems Children Will Sit Still For*. New York: Citation Press.

Dewey, John. 1933. *How We Think*. Boston: D.C. Health.

Egsgard, John C. 1969. "Geometry All Around Us—K–12." *Arithmetic Teacher* 16: 437–445.

Elkind, David. 1974. *Children and Adolescents*. 2d ed. New York: Oxford University Press.

Enstrom, E.A., and Doris Enstrom. 1966. "Numerals Still Count." *Arithmetic Teacher* 13: 131–134.

Fehr, Howard F., and Jo McKeeby Phillips. 1967. *Teaching Modern Mathematics in the Elementary School*. Reading, Mass.: Addison-Wesley.

Franco, Laura, and R.W. Sperry. 1977. "Hemisphere Lateralization for Cognitive Processing of Geometry." *Neuropsychologia* 15: 107–114.

Frostig, Marianne, and Phyllis Maslow. 1973. *Learning Problems in the Classroom*. New York: Grune and Stratton.

Gagné, Robert M. 1977. *The Conditions of Learning*. 3d ed. New York: Holt, Rinehart and Winston.

Gagné, Robert M., and Leslie J. Briggs. 1978. *Principles of Instructional Design*. 2d ed. New York: Holt, Rinehart and Winston.

Gallagher, James. 1975. *Teaching the Gifted Child*. 2d ed. Boston: Allyn and Bacon.

Gattegno, C. 1956. "New Developments in Arithmetic Teaching in Britain." *Arithmetic Teacher* 3: 85–89.

Gelman, Rachel, and C.R. Gallistel. 1978. *The Child's Understanding of Number*. Cambridge: Harvard University Press.

Gesell, Arnold; Frances L. Ilg; and Louise Bates Ames. 1946. *The Child from Five to Ten*. New York: Harper and Row.

Ginsburg, Herbert. 1977. *Children's Arithmetic: The Learning Process*. New York: D. Van Nostrand.

Glennon, Vincent J. 1965. "And Now Synthesis: A Theoretical Model for Mathematics Education." *Arithmetic Teacher* 12: 134–141.

Glennon, Vincent J., ed. 1981. *Mathematics Education for Exceptional Children and Youth*. Reston, Va.: National Council of Teachers of Mathematics.

Good, Thomas L., and Douglas A Grows. 1975. "Process-Product Relationships in a Fourth-Grade Classroom." Washington, D.C.: NIE. (ERIC document no. 125907.)

Gundlach, Bernard H. 1969. "The History of Numbers and Numerals." In *Historical Topics for the Mathematics Classroom*. Thirty-first Yearbook of the National Council of Teachers of Mathematics. Washington, D.C.: The Council.

Hildreth, Gertrude. 1936. *Learning the Three Rs*. Minneapolis: Education Publishers.

Hill, Winfred. 1963. *Learning*. San Francisco: Chandler.

Hofstadter, Douglas R. 1979. *Gödel, Escher, and Bach: An Eternal Golden Braid*. New York: Basic Books.

Hollister, George E., and Agnes G. Gunderson. 1954. *Teaching Arithmetic in Grades I and II*. Boston: D.C. Heath.

Hutchings, Barton. 1976. *Low Stress Algorithms*. College Park: University of Maryland Arithmetic Center.

Ilg, Frances, and Louise B. Ames. 1951. "Developmental Trends in Arithmetic." *Journal of Genetic Psychology* 79: 3–28.

Inhelder, B., and Jean Piaget. 1958. *The Growth of Logical Thinking from Childhood to Adolescence*. London: Routledge and Kegan Paul.

Jackson, Lambert Lincoln. 1906. *The Educational Significance of Sixteenth Century Arithmetic*. New York: Teachers College, Columbia University.

Johnson, Doris J., and Helmer R. Myklebust. 1971. *Learning Disabilities*. New York: Grune and Stratton.

Johnson, Stanley W. 1979. *Arithmetic and Learning Disabilities*. Boston: Allyn and Bacon.

Jordon, Dale R. 1977. *Dyslexia in the Classroom*. 2d ed. Columbus, Ohio: Charles E. Merrill.

Kaliski, Lotte. 1962. "Arithmetic and the Brain-Injured Child." *Arithmetic Teacher* 9: 245–251.

Kamii, Constance. 1972. "An Application of Piaget's Theory to the Conceptualization of a Preschool Curriculum" In *The Preschool in Action: Exploring Early Childhood Programs*, edited by Ronald K. Parker. Boston: Allyn and Bacon.

Kamii, Constance, and Rheta De Vries. 1976. *Piaget, Children and Number*. Washington, D.C.: National Association for the Education of Young Children.

Karpinski, Louis Charles. 1925. *The History of Arithmetic*. Chicago: Rand McNally.

Knifong, J. Dan. 1973. "Discovering Pupils' Preconception of Physical Phenomena." *School Science and Mathematics* 73: 23–28.

Knifong, J. Dan, and Grace M. Burton. 1979. "Chisanbop: Just Another Kind of Finger Reckoning?" *Arithmetic Teacher* 26(7): 14–17.

———. Forthcoming. "Understanding Word Problems." *Arithmetic Teacher*.

Kofsky, Ellin. 1966. "A Scalogram Study of Classificatory Development." *Child Development* 37: 191–204.

Kolers, Paul A. 1968. "Some Psychological Aspects of Pattern Recognition." In *Recognizing Patterns: Studies in Living and Automated Systems*, edited by Paul A. Kolers and Murray Eden. Cambridge: MIT Press.

Kurtz, V. Ray. 1978. "Kindergarten Mathematics—A Survey." *Arithmetic Teacher* 25(8): 51–53.

Labinowicz, Ed. 1980. *The Piaget Primer*. Menlo Park, Calif.: Addison-Wesley.

Lee, Lee C. 1965. "Concept Utilization in Preschool Children." *Child Development* 36: 221–227.

Leslie, John. 1817. *The Philosophy of Arithmetic*. Edinburgh: Abernathy and Walker.

Lieberthal, Edwin M. 1979. *The Complete Book of Fingermath*. New York: McGraw-Hill.

Longstreth, Langdon E. 1968. *Psychological Development of the Child*. New York: The Ronald Press.

Lovell, John W. 1827. *Introductory Arithmetic Prepared for the Pupils of the Lancasterian Schools*. New Haven: S. Wadsworth.

Lovell, Kenneth. 1971. *The Growth of Understanding in Mathematics: Kindergarten Through Grade Three*. New York: Holt, Rinehart and Winston.

Maslow, Abraham H. 1968. *Toward a Psychology of Being*. 2d ed. Princeton, N.J.: Van Hostrand.

McKillip, William D. 1970. "Patterns—A Mathematical Unit for Three- and Four-Year-Olds." *Arithmetic Teacher* 17: 15–18.

Meltzer, Lynn J. 1978. "Abstract Reasoning in a Specific Group of Perceptually Impaired Children; Namely, the Learning Disabled." *Journal of Genetic Psychology* 132: 185–195.

Miller, James O., and Janet C. Camp. 1972. "Toward Individual Competency—A Curriculum in the Child's Ecology." In *The Preschool in Action: Exploring Early Childhood Programs*, edited by Ronald K. Parker. Boston: Allyn and Bacon.

Monroe, Walter Scott. 1917. *Development of Arithmetic as a School Subject*. Bureau of Education Bulletin, No. 10. Washington, D.C.: Government Printing Office.

Moore, Eliakim Hastings. 1967. "On the Foundations of Mathematics." *Mathematics Teacher* 60: 360–374.

Morton, Robert Lee. 1938. *Teaching Arithmetic in the Elementary School*. Vol. II, *Intermediate School*. New York: Silver Burdett.

Moyer, John C., and Margaret Bannockie Moyer. 1978. "Computation: Implications for Learning-Disabled Children." In *Developing Computation Skills*. 1978 Yearbook of the National Council of Teachers of Mathematics. Reston, Va.: The Council.

National Council of Teachers of Mathematics. 1980. *An Agenda for Action: Recommendations for School Mathematics in the 1980s*. Reston, Va.: The Council.

North Carolina Department of Public Instruction. 1977. *Course of Study for Elementary and Secondary Schools K–12*. Raleigh: State Department of Public Instruction.

Nuffield Foundation. 1972. *Mathematics Begins*. New York: John Wiley.

Olson, Lynn. 1969. "The Meaning of Meaningful." *Arithmetic Teacher* 16: 276–280.

Phillips, John L. 1969. *The Origin of Intellect: Piaget's Theory*. San Francisco: W.H. Freeman.

Piaget, Jean. 1950. *The Psychology of Intelligence*. London: Routledge and Kegan Paul.

———. 1952. *The Child's Conception of Number*. London: Routledge and Kegan Paul.

———. 1967. *Six Psychological Studies*. New York: Random House.

———. 1970. *Science of Education and the Psychology of the Child*. New York: Orion Press.

Pirsig, Robert M. 1975. *Zen and the Art of Motorcycle Maintenance*. New York: Bantam Books.

Post, Thomas R. 1981. "Fractions: Results and Implications from National Assessment. *Arithmetic Teacher* 28(9): 26–31.

Rea, Robert E., and Robert E. Reys. 1971. "Competencies of Entering Kindergarteners in Geometry, Number, Money, and Measurement." *School Science and Mathematics* 71: 389–402.

Readings in Behavior Modification. 1978. Guilford, Conn.: Special Learning Corp.

Reed, Homer B. 1927. *Psychology of Elementary School Subjects*. Boston: Ginn and Co.

Reisman, Fredricka. 1978. *A Guide to the Diagnostic Teaching of Arithmetic*. 2d ed. Columbus, Ohio: Charles E. Merrill.

Richardson, Lloyd I., et al. 1980. *A Mathematics Activity Curriculum for Early Childhood and Special Education*. New York: Macmillan.

Rosenquist, Lucy Lynde. 1949. *Young Children Learn to Use Arithmetic*. Boston: Ginn and Co.

Rosenthal, Robert, and Lenore F. Jacobson. 1968. *Pygmalian in the Classroom*. New York: Rinehart and Winston.

Rowe, Mary Budd. 1978. "Wait, Wait, Wait. . . ." *School Science and Mathematics* 78: 207–216.

Sahakian, William S. 1970. *Psychology of Learning*. Chicago: Markham.

Sandburg, Carl. 1950. *Complete Poems*. New York: Harcourt, Brace and World.

Schaeffer, Benson; Valeria H. Eggleston; and Judy L. Scott. 1974. "Number Development in Young Children." *Cognitive Psychology* 6: 357–379.

Schifani, John W.; Robert M. Anderson; and Sara J. Odle, eds. 1980. *Implementing Learning in the Least Restrictive Environment*. Baltimore: University Park Press.

Schminke, C.W., and Enoch Dumas. 1981. *Math Activities for Child Involvement*. 3d ed. Boston: Allyn and Bacon.

Shookoohi, Gholam-Hossein. 1978. "Manipulative Devices for Teaching Place Value." *Arithmetic Teacher* 25: 49–51.

Silverstein, Shel. *Where the Sidewalk Ends*. 1971. New York: Harper and Row.

Skemp. Richard. 1973. *The Psychology of Learning Mathematics*. New York: Penguin Books.

Skinner, B.F. 1948. *Walden II*. New York: Macmillan.

———. 1968. *The Technology of Teaching*. Englewood Cliffs, N.J.: Prentice-Hall.

———. 1971. *Beyond Freedom and Dignity*. New York: Alfred A. Knopf.

Smith, David Eugene. 1922. *The Teaching of Elementary Mathematics*. New York: Macmillan.

———. 1959. *A Sourcebook in Mathematics*. Vol I. New York: Dover Publications.

Smith, David Eugene, and Jekuthiel Ginsburg. 1934. *A History of Mathematics in America Before 1900*. Chicago: Open Court.

Smith, Henry Lester; Merrill T. Eaton; and Kathleen Dugdale. 1945. *One Hundred Fifty Years of Arithmetic Textbooks*. Bloomington: Bulletin of the School of Education, Indiana University.

Spitzer, Dean R. 1972. *Concept Formation and Learning in Early Childhood*. Columbus, Ohio: Charles E. Merrill.

Spradin, Joseph E., et al. 1974. "Performance of Mentally Retarded Children on Pre-Arithmetic Tasks." *American Journal of Mental Deficiency* 78: 397–403.

Stern, Catherine. 1949. *Children Discover Arithmetic*. New York: Harper and Brothers.

Stern, Catherine, and Margaret B. Stern. 1971. *Children Discover Arithmetic*. New York: Harper and Row.

Stevenson, P.R. 1925. "Difficulties in Problem Solving." *Journal of Educational Research* 9: 95–103.

Suydam, Marilyn N. 1982. "Update on Research on Problem Solving: Implications for Classroom Teaching." *Arithmetic Teacher* 29(6): 56–60.

Suydam, Marilyn N., and Fred Weaver. 1975. "Research on Mathematics Learning." In *Mathematics Learning in Early Childhood*, edited by Joseph Payne. Reston, Va.: National Council of Teachers of Mathematics.

Thorndike, Edward L. 1921. *The New Methods in Arithmetic*. Chicago: Rand McNally.

Thurber, Donald M. 1978. *D'Nealian Handwriting*. Palo Alto, Calif.: Scott, Foresman.

Troutman, Andria P., and Betty K. Lichtenberg. 1982. *Mathematics: A Good Beginning*. 2d ed. Monterey, Calif.: Brooks/Cole.

Uhr, Leonard, 1973. *Pattern Recognition, Learning and Thought*. Englewood Cliffs, N.J.: Prentice-Hall.

Underhill, Robert G. 1977. *Teaching Elementary School Mathematics*. 2d ed. Columbus, Ohio: Charles E. Merrill.

Upton, Clifford B. 1935. "Making Long Division Automatic." In *The Teaching of Arithmetic*. Tenth Yearbook of the National Council of Teachers of Mathematics. New York: Bureau of Publications, Teachers College. Columbia University.

Usiskin, Zalman. 1979. "Applications in Elementary Algebra and Geometry." In *Applications in School Mathematics*, edited by Sidney Sharron and Robert E. Reys. Reston, Va.: National Council of Teachers of Mathematics.

Van de Walle, John, and Charles S. Thompson. 1981. "A Poster-Board Balance Helps Write Equations." *Arithmetic Teacher* 28(9): 4–8.

Vernon, M.D. 1952. *Further Study of Visual Perception*. zn: Cambridge University Press.

Wang, Margaret C.; Lauren B. Resnick; and Robert F. Boozer. 1971. "The Sequence of Development of Some Early Mathematics Behaviors." *Child Development* 42: 1767–1778.

White, William F. 1908. *A Scrapbook of Elementary Mathematics*. Chicago: Open Court.

Williams, J.D. 1971. *Teaching Techniques in Primary Maths*. London: National Foundation for Educational Research in England and Wales.

Wilson, Guy M., and C.O. Dalrymple. 1937. "Useful Fractions." *Journal of Educational Research* 30: 341–347.

Winick, Mariann. 1973. *Before the 3 Rs*. New York: David McKay.

Wirtz, Robert. 1974. *Drill and Practice at the Problem-Solving Level*. Washington, D.C.: Curriculum Development Associates.

Wittrock, M.C. 1978. "Education and the Cognitive Processes of the Brain." In *Education and the Brain*, edited by Jeanne S. Chall and Allan F. Mirsky. Seventy-seventh Yearbook of the National Society for the Study of Education, Part II. Chicago: University of Chicago Press.

Wohlwill, Joachim F. 1960. "A Study of the Development of the Number Concept by Scalogram Analysis." *Journal of Genetic Psychology* 97: 345–377.

Wolford, Daniel. 1924. *The Child's Mind and the Common Branches*. New York: Macmillan.

Woody, Thomas. 1929. *A History of Women's Education in the United States*. Vols. I and II. New York: Science Press.

Young, Sharon. 1979. *Mathematics in Children's Books*. Palo Alto, Calif.: Creative Publications.

index

AAB pattern, 50–51
AB pattern, 49
ABA pattern, 49
Abacus, 196–197, 201–202
Activities
  classification, 39–43
  counting, 59–68, 98–104
  cut-and-paste, 40
  fractions, 207–208
  geometry, 151, 153–154
  graphing, 171–172
  measurement, 158–167
  number(s), 93–94, 98–105
  numerals, 76–77, 80–88
  patterning, 50–51
  picture matching, 107
  place value, 180–181, 185–187
  relationships, 53–54
  seriation, 45–47
  sets, 141
  subtraction, 141–144
Adaptive behavior, 26
Addition, 11, 125, 126, 127–136, 138–139, 188, 189, 190–192, 139
  algorithms for, 188, 189, 190–192, 193
  inverse of, 138–139
  models for, 127–136

Addition facts, 175
Agenda for Action, An, 20
Algorithms, 20, 111, 188–204
  addition, 188, 189, 190–192, 193
  and materials, 194–198
  and mechanical aids, 201–203
  and pencil and paperwork, 198–201
  rote learning of, 198–199
  subtraction, 188, 192–193, 201
  whole number, 193–194
American Association on Mental Deficiency, 26
Ames, Louise B., 1–2
"And Now Synthesis," 9
Area, 159
Aristotle, 14
"Arithmetic," 91
Arithmetic Readiness Inventory, 122
Arithmetic Teacher, 9
Art of Numbrynge, The, 198
Assessment, 112–124
Awareness exercise, 89–90

Back-to-basics movement, 19–20
Balance beam, 134–136, 145
Baratta-Lorton, Mary, 5, 6, 27, 36, 51, 80, 87, 105, 125–126, 129, 170–171, 182, 207, 232
Base-10 numeration, 51
Basic word lists, 110, 111
Battery board, 100
Bay, Joseph C., 98, 128
Bereiter, Carl, 19
Birch, Herbert G., 7
Blind children, 28, 29
Bradford, E.J.G., 189
Braille, 28, 30
Brueckner, Leo J., 122, 142
Bruner, Jerome S., 95, 228
Brownell, William H., 17, 122–123
Buckingham, B. R., 189
Burton, Grace, 4, 126, 137, 173

Camp, Janet C., 7
Capacity, 159–161
Cardinal numbers, 109–110
Chisanbop, 137

Classification, 37–44
   materials, 38
   tasks, 38–44
Colburn, Warren,
   12–13, 194
Cognitive level, tests
   for, 119–121
Committee of Ten, 149
Comparison questions,
   139–140
Computation, 10, 19
Concept attainment,
   106–108
Concept formation of
   number, 96–98
Concepts, 164
Concrete operational
   stage, 26–27
Connectionism, 15–16,
   17
Conservation of
   number, 92–94
Counting, 57–68,
   127–128, 137
   books for, 58–59
   fingerplays for,
      59–62
   songs for, 62–68
   verses for, 59–68
Counting rods, 202
Counting task, 96–98
Coxford, Arthur F.,
   Jr., 106–108, 156
*Crafte of Numbrynge,
   The*, 190,
   192–193, 198

Cruisenaire rods, 83,
   97, 133–134, 159,
   181, 184
Cut-and-paste
   activities, 40

Deaf children, 30–31
   emotional problems
      of, 30
   learning tasks for, 31
Decomposition
   method, 201
Dewey, John, 14–15,
   16
Diagnosis, 112–123
Difference train,
   41–42
Dilworth, Thomas, 11
Distar, 19
Dominance, 74–75
Dot sets, 103

Educating children
   with special
   needs, 22–36
Education for All
   Handicapped
   Children Act of
   1975, 22–23, 24,
   29, 123
Educational eras,
   10–20
   back-to-basics
      movement, 19–20
   colonial era, 10–11

early national
   period, 11–13
early twentieth
   century, 15–16
post-Sputnik era,
   18–19
Eicholz, Robert, 130
Eggard, John C., 152
Elkind, David, 45
Eliot, T. S., 214
Emberly, Barbara, 65
Emotionally
   handicapped
   children, 24, 34
Engleman, Siegfried,
   19
Equivalence
   relationships,
   55–56
ESS, 43
Environment of
   preschool
   children, 1–4
Expectations of
   kindergarten
   teachers, 216–217

Facts, 164
Fading technique, 70
Feely box, 39–40, 41
Fingermath, 137
Fish, Daniel W., 135
5 – 3, 138–141, 142,
   143, 145–146
5 – 2, 137, 144

*First Lessons in
    Intellectual
    Arithmetic on the
    Plan of Pestalozzi*,
    12–13
Fractions, 205–209
Franklin, Benjamin, 10
Frisuis, Gemma, 191

Gagné, Robert M., 95,
    122
Geometry, 147–154
    activities, 151,
        153–154
    at kindergarten
        entrance,
        147–148
    in kindergarten
        curriculum,
        149–153
Gesell, Arnold, 166
Gestalt psychology,
    16–17
Generalizing, 27
Gifted children, 35–36
    suggestions for
        teaching, 35
Glennon, Vincent J., 9
Goals for Teaching,
    1–8
    kindergarten
        mathematics, 6–8
Graphing, 168–173
Grube, W. W., 14
Gunderson, Agnes C.,
    112, 115–116

Gussow, Joan Pye, 7

Hall, G. Stanley, 14
Handicapped children,
    22–34, 157–158
    emotionally
        handicapped, 24,
        34
    health impaired, 24,
        34
    hearing
        handicapped,
        30–31
    learning disabled,
        24, 31–33,
        157–158
    mentally retarded,
        24, 25–288
    orthopedically
        handicapped, 24,
        33–34
    speech impaired, 24,
        34
    visually
        handicapped, 24,
        28–30
Health-impaired
    children, 24, 34
Hearing-handicapped
    children, 24,
    30–31
Hildreth, Gertrude,
    211–212
Hollister, George E.,
    112, 115–116
Horizontal notation,
    199

Hundred board, 85–87
Hutchings, Barton,
    192
Hypotheses and
    conclusions, 2

Ilg, Frances, 1–2
Individual Educational
    Plan (IEP), 24,
    33, 123
Individual
    Mathematics
    Readiness
    Inventory,
    114–116
Inexpensive materials,
    232–233
Inverse of addition,
    138–139
Iowa Test of Preschool
    Development, 122

James, William, 14–15

K-12 geometry
    curriculu, 152
Keats, Ezra Jack,
    62–63
KeyMath, 113
Kindergarten
    mathematics
    programs, 6–8
Knifong, J. Dan, 4,
    126, 137, 173

Kolers, Paul A., 49
Kraner Preschool Math
    Inventory, 122

Lancaster, Joseph, 13
Lancastrian plan, 13
Learning-disabled
    children, 24,
    31–33, 157–158
    definition of, 31–32
Learning problems, 23
Left-right orientation,
    72
Length, 158–159
Leslie, John, 191
Lesson plans, 234–237
Locke, John, 15
Logico-mathematical
    knowledge, 91–92

Mainstreaming,
    22–23, 24
"Make a Matrix," 43
Manipulative materials
    for algorithms,
    194–199
Mann-Suiter
    Developmental
    Arithmatic
    Inventory, 122
Maslow, Abraham, 229
Mass, 161–162
*Math Readiness
    Vocabulary and
    Concepts*, 39

Mathematics Begins,
    53–54
Mathematics program,
    characteristics of,
    213–214
Mathematics Their Way,
    6, 36
Measurement, 10, 21,
    155–167
    activities, 155,
    158–169
    definitions, 156
    incoming skills,
    155–156
    special problems,
    157–158
Memorizing number
    facts, 173–178
Mentally retarded
    children, 24,
    25–28
    curriculum for, 28
Metric system,
    241–242
Miller, James O., 7
Milne, A.A., 62
Model sets, 81–85
Moderately retarded
    children, 26
Money, 163–166
Montessori, Maria,
    133, 161, 162,
    184, 185
Moore, E. H., 6
Morton, Robert Lee,
    193

Moyer, John C., 32
Multiplication, 11–12,
    51

National Council of
    Teachers of
    Mathematics, 20
"New Basics," 20
*New Complete System of
    Arithmetic*, 11
"New math," 18–19,
    149
Non-proportional
    materials,
    185–187
Number-fact chart,
    176
Number facts,
    173–178
Number line, 85,
    130–134, 142–149
Nuffield Guides,
    53–54
Number(s), 3, 11, 13,
    15, 19, 21, 47, 80,
    98–101, 173–178
    concept of, 91–108
    conservation of,
    92–94
    counting task,
    96–98
    definitions of, 92
    developing concepts
    of, 94–96
    number stations, 105
Number stations, 105

Numeral cards, 80
Numeral recognition, 79–90
Numerals, 7, 11, 21, 69–87

Olson, Lynn, 207
One-to-one correspondence, 96–97, 109
One Wide River to Cross, 68
Opticon, 28
Ordinal numbers, 109–110
Orthopedically handicapped children, 24, 33–34

Palmer, Hap, 39
Parent participation in teaching, 4–6, 177
Partial sums, 200–201
Patterning, 48–52
  activities, 50–51
  theory of, 48–49
  types of, 49–50
Pavlov, Ivan, 228
Pencil and paper for algorithms, 198–201
Penmanship, 71–72

Perceptually handicapped children, 24, 28–31
Physical knowledge, 91–92
Piaget, Jean, 26, 37, 44, 48, 83, 91, 92–94, 106–107, 112, 122, 125, 154, 156, 158, 159, 229–230
Picture matching activities, 101
Place value, 179–187
  and remediation, 182–187
Plato, 14, 15
Pocket calculator, 203
Pocket chart, 195
Positive teaching, 1–8
Premack, David, 230
Preschool learning, 1–4
Principles of Psychology, 14
Problem-solving, 20, 27, 165–166, 210–212
Proportional materials, 184–185
Proportional rods, 133
Psychological terms, 228–231

Questions for adults, 3–4

Rea, Robert E., 147–148, 155–156, 161, 166
Recitation, rote and paced, 97
Recorde, Robert, 188
Reed, Homer B., 16
Reys, Robert E., 147–148, 155–156, 161, 166
Reflexive property, 55–56
Relationships, 53–56
Remediation, 123–124, 182–187
  guidelines for, 124
  and place value, 182–187
Rote learning of algorithms, 198–199
Rowe, Mary Budd, 212

Sandburg, Carl, 69, 91
Schoolmaster's Assistant, the, 11
Seriation, 45–47
Sets, 129–130, 139–141
Silverstein, Shel, 163

Skills, 164–165
Skinner, B. F., 19, 70, 229, 230
Smith, David Eugene, 190
Sorting box, 102
Spatial relations, 150
Speech-impaired children, 24, 34
Speer, William W., 97, 99
Sputnik, 18
Stern, Catherine, 17, 83
Stern counting board, 181
Stevenson, P. R., 189
Stone, John, 16, 127
Strip cards, 81–82
Subtraction, 11, 125–126, 136–146, 188, 192–193, 201
    algorithms for, 188, 192–193, 201
    models for, 136–144
Suppliers of math resources, 218
Symmetric property, 55–56
Synthesis of mathematics education, 9, 20–21

Teachers and parents, 4–6
Teaching early grades, 4–8
Teaching machines, 19
Technical terms, 110–111
Temperature, 162
Ten basic skills areas, 239–240
Testing number facts, 177
Thorndike, E. G., 15–16, 17, 19, 137
Time, 166–167
Transitive property, 55–56

Uhr, Leonard, 48
Underhill, Robert G., 122
Upton, Clifford B., 188–189

Vertical notation, 199–200
Visual stimulation, 29
Visually handicapped children, 24, 28–30
Vocabulary development, technical problems in, 109–111

Volume, 159–161

Walk-on number line, 104
Wertheimer, Max, 17
Wiebe, Edward, 148, 149
Weight, 161–162
White, E. E., 129
White, William F., 202
Williams, J. D., 204
Wirtz, Robert, 196–197
Wirtz ten-frame, 181
Wolford, Daniel, 189
Woody, Thomas, 11, 12
Workjobs for Parents, 5
Workjobs II, 27, 36, 207
Writing numerals, 69–78
    dealing with reversals, 72–74
    instructional techniques, 70, 75–78

Young Man's Companion, the, 10

Zero, 88–89